The Ultimate Keto Diet for Beginners

Easy and Healthy Keto Recipes to Lose Weight, Boost Brain Health, Reverse Disease, and Lower Blood Pressure (Lose Up to 30 Pounds in 21-Day)

Dr Jacar Kalten

Table of contents

Introduction

Many trends around the world have encouraged the masses to become self-aware of their diets. As we step forward in the 21st century, a new disease has become a concern, which is called obesity. It is the cause of many chronic diseases that hinder the quality of life and decreases mortality by introducing different diseases into our body. It exists because people do not care about what they eat or how much they're eating. To promote a healthy lifestyle, common people started to follow different diets all over the world. One of the most popular diets that have made people talking about it for a decade is the keto diet.

A keto diet is a diet that focuses more on high consumption of fat, adequate consumption of protein coma, and very low consumption of carbohydrates. Its main objective is to change the basic nutrient for energy from carbohydrates to fats. This was mainly used to treat patients with epilepsy and other cognitive diseases but now is popular for achieving weight loss and encouraging a healthy lifestyle also.

Does this pique your interest to try the keto diet? But do you know where you should start? Don't worry, I have got you covered with detailed information about the marvelous ketogenic diet. Moreover, this cookbook contains a meal plan and quick and tasty recipes that will help your transition to keto diet effectively.

Chapter 1: The Basics of The Keto Diet

What is the keto diet?

The Ketogenic diet is like many other diets that require you to lower your carbohydrate intake. Similar to the Atkin diet and low carb diet, you are encouraged to eat protein like poultry and fat heavy products, which are encouraged to be acquired by plant sources such as avocado. By decreasing the level of carbohydrate available, the body shifts its physiology and starts breaking down fat for energy. The product of this breakdown is ketone bodies which place is glucose in providing nutrition to the brain. The body then goes into the state of ketosis, which is high levels of ketones in the body.

It was discovered as a treatment for epilepsy in 1921 by Dr. Russell Wilder, who came up with the term "Ketogenic diet." With the introduction of anticonvulsant, the popularity of keto diet shrank. It had its revival when the famous Hollywood producer, John Abrahim's son was successfully treated by the ketogenic diet in 2007. Afterward, a lot of differences went into the diet, exposing its numerous benefits.

The ketogenic diet is a very beneficial diet that can reduce the likelihood of chronic diseases and illnesses even though its benefits are known, the mechanism of how it does that is still unclear. It is believed that overall it reduces oxidative stress in the cells all over the body.

How is keto different from other diets?

Keto diet is not an overly restrictive diet, but it has many variations according to people's needs. All variation has a little bit of difference but is mainly the same. Keto diet is very different from other diets in many ways.

- Keto diet

Generally, the ketogenic diet triggers ketones inside the body and increases it to a higher level than normal. It requires the person to get more calories, almost 75%, from fats. The person avoids getting calories from carbohydrates, reducing it to 5%. The rest can be provided by proteins and other sources. It helps to increase the breakdown of fat, balancing out the body composition.

- Other low-calorie diets

Their main objective is to decrease the carbohydrate intake so that the body composition becomes stable. They focus on only the aspect of the decreasing carbohydrate from the daily routine, almost less than 30% of the energy is required by carbohydrate which is lower than normal but not enough to initiate ketosis in the body as ketogenic diet does. Even though the levels of carbohydrate decrease in the body, it will still be high enough to render breaking down of fat unnecessary.

- Atkin diet

This is most often confused with the ketogenic diet because they both restrict the use of carbohydrates. In this diet, the person eats less than 20 grams of carbohydrate daily. The calories are compensated by increasing the use of fat and mainly proteins. At first, carbohydrate consumption is restricted, but later on, it is again reintroduced to a tolerable level. In this diet, protein consumption is a little higher than in a ketogenic diet.

- Paleo diet

In this form of dieting, the person consumes only the foods that were available to a paleolithic man. It means a person cannot eat any type of processed food or grains. They also cannot eat sugar and legumes and have to consume fruits, vegetables, nuts, and meat. The macronutrient structure is not planned in this diet, so the amount of protein and fat may increase indefinitely. The levels of carbohydrate to get ketosis is not nearly enough to initiate the breakdown of fat in the Paleo diet.

How does the ketogenic diet work?

Our bodies have been using glucose as the main energy-providing molecule that is a form of carbohydrate; hence carbohydrate is the primary source of energy. In certain cases, when the body is receiving less than 20 to 50-gram carbohydrates for 2 to 4 days, the cells are starved for energy, and they have to find a new source. The cells of the body start to break down fat in the state of "starvation" to make a substitute for glucose for energy.

The body uses the process of fatty acid oxidation, which occurs inside the mitochondria of cells. In this process, three ketone bodies are produced, which replaces glucose as the source. This process occurs inside the liver. The body can also use proteins in a process called gluconeogenesis to produce glucose, but proteins are mainly used for growth and repair and cannot only be used for this purpose.

By burning off excess fats that are stored in our body, our body's composition and endurance become stable. We get more adapted to process fats in a daily routine. This helps to lower the levels of fats, which, in return, saves us from many other diseases and helps in weight loss.

How to know when you are in Ketosis

In the state of ketogenic dieting, your body goes through many changes that include reduction and glucose and insulin levels. There are many other small and big changes throughout your body that may be classified as positive or negative.

- Fruity smell breath

The person going ketoses usually report bad breath for fruity smell breath. People following Atkin and other low-carb diets also sometimes report this phenomenon. This is because the ketone bodies produce a smell that is released from the mouth. It is mainly because of the ketone body, acetone.
People going through ketosis or following this diet need to brush more times, or manage their breath using sugar-free gum for sugar-free drinks. Make sure to check for labels of carbohydrate in them.

- Weight loss

The ketogenic diet, along with other low carb diets, shows significant weight loss in both short and long terms. The short term is usually by the loss of water and carbohydrate stores, while in the long term is by steady fat stores decline. A significant amount of weight loss can be seen in just a few months.

- Increased level of ketones in the blood

The most reliable way to check that you are going through ketosis is to check blood for ketone bodies. A meter is available to check BHB (beta-hydroxybutyrate) levels by using just a needle. Unfortunately, it can be expensive, and not everyone can use it.

- Ketones in urine

As methods of checking ketone levels get inexpensive, also their reliability is compromised. In the state of nutritional ketosis, urine excretes more ketones, especially acetoacetate from your body. This can be checked by using special indicator strips.

- Feeling less hungry

Though the main mechanism is not known, it is believed that following a ketogenic diet reduces appetite in an individual. It may be due to increased intake of vegetables and protein and alteration of the hunger hormone.

- Being energetic

People following the ketogenic diet report to feel more energetic and active than before. It gives the brain more clarity and helps it, which is not surprising because this diet was used to treat brain diseases. Once adapted, high energy fat will fuel all the brain's functions effectively.

- Short term fatigue

At the beginning of the diet, a person might feel less focused and tired because the body is shifting from using glucose to ketones. This takes about one week, but after that, the effects wear off.

- Insomnia

One of the key problems that the dieter's report is sleeplessness. It is an initial symptom of this diet, but it gets better after a few weeks.

- Digestive issues

When your body is not used to the diet, initially, you will feel lots of digestive issues such as diarrhea and constipation. It is advised that you consume more green leafy vegetables, which are high in fiber in the first days.

The Health Benefits of Keto diet

There are numerous benefits of a ketogenic diet, which improves overall health and quality of life. It gets rid of many diseases.

- Helps in weight loss

Like other low carb diets, the ketogenic diet also shows a drastic decrease in weight loss, so if someone is going through obesity or wants to lose weight, they should start the ketogenic diet.
Many studies show that it is an effective way, and meta-analysis of 13 different controlled randomized trials showed that ketogenic diet works.

- Being energized

After getting used to the ketogenic diet, a person gets more active and do a lot more than before. Also, they report fewer happenings of fatigue. This can lead to a more fulfilling life.

- Reduces acne

Sugar fluctuations are most likely the culprit of acne. Eating a lot of refined and processed food can raise blood sugar levels significantly, which affects skin health. By following the ketogenic diet and eating fewer carbohydrates, acne could be controlled.

- Reduces the chances of cancer

The ketogenic diet is under a lot of studies to show its effect on cancer. One study has found that the diet can be used as complementary with radiation and chemotherapy. It is mainly because it reduces the level of oxidative stress. Also, it reduces glucose, which could be the main source of nutrition for cancers.

- Increases heart health

The diet has shown to increase levels of HDL, which are good fats and decrease levels of LDL, which are bad fats. Also, dieters have less amount of cholesterol in the blood as well.

- Reduces seizures

Increased levels of ketones in our body reduce the chances of seizures. It is highly effective and was used as the main treatment for it for a long time. Ketosis results in beneficial development in the brain.

Helpful Tips for the keto Journey

Starting a ketogenic diet is a healthy step towards a good life, but it is important to note that every change is difficult at first. You might feel lethargic and unmotivated initially, but if you go through, you will undoubtedly reap the benefits. Some ways to make you stay on track include:

- Lower carbohydrate consumption

One of the most important things in this diet is to lower your carbohydrate intake. You can do that by avoiding to eat processed and refined foods and switching to proteins and fats. This does not mean you are strictly prohibited from eating any type of sugar do you need to be mindful of the calories to intake. Reduce your carbs diet to less than 20 grams/day.

- Increase physical activity

Once you get used to the ketogenic diet, you start feeling more energized and active. This new form of energy can be used in exercise and other physical tasks. During exercise and physical tasks, you will burn off more glycogen and decrease your glucose level, further initiating ketosis quickly. Glycogen is glucose reserves in your body.

- Add more coconut oil in your diet

Coconut oil is shown to help in many different studies. It contains a special type of fat called MCT (medium-chain triglycerides), which readily absorbed in the liver, which causes quick change to its byproducts, the ketone bodies. Coconut oil contains four types of MCT, but the most important is lauric acid. This causes steady ketosis in the long run.

- Regulate Protein Intake

It is important that the person takes adequate protein intake while going through a ketogenic diet. If too low protein is consumed, then the body starts to do gluconeogenesis, which is the process of making glucose from proteins, causing muscle wasting. On the other hand, if too much protein is eaten, then the effects of gluconeogenesis will prevent ketosis from developing.

- Increase healthy fats

Getting your fat from a healthy source is just as important as minimizing your carbohydrate intake in this diet. It should be taken from both animal and plant-based forms. You can eat avocado, olive oil, or butter, but if you need to lose weight, then take care of the calories your intake as fats.

- Do fasting

Even when treating epilepsy in the past century, children were required to fast for a day or two to quickly initiate ketosis. If you are using this diet, then a few hours of not eating anything or not eating fats will put you in ketosis quickly.

- Hire a nutritionist

Calculating calories and knowing what you need to eat can be a little overwhelming for some people. If you are experiencing difficulties in following the diet, then you should ask for help from a professional.

- Check your ketones levels

This diet varies from individual to individual, so to make informed changes, you need to keep checking your own levels. There are many ways to do so from breathalyzer, urine strip test, and blood strip tests. If you can afford it, then a blood test is the most reliable.

Chapter 2: Foods to Eat

To start your Keto diet journey, here is a list of food that you need to eat.

Protein:

- Pasteurized pork
- Grass-fed beef, pork, lamb, goat, and other meat
- Wild-caught fish and seafood
- Egg, pasteurized

Fats:

- Avocado
- Coconut oil
- Olive oil
- MCT oil
- Coconut butter
- Peanut butter
- All nut and seed-based butter, unsweetened
- Heavy cream, full-fat
- Coconut cream
- Coconut yogurt
- Greek yogurt, organic, full-fat

Carbs:

Vegetables – All the vegetables that grow above the ground and rich in fiber, such as

- Spinach
- Arugula

- Celery

- Asparagus

- Leeks

- Squash

- Eggplants

- Onion

- Bell peppers

- Zucchini

- Rutabaga

- Kale

Fruits – All the fruits that are low in glycemic index and less in sugar

- Strawberry

- Blueberry

- Blackberry

- Raspberry

- Star fruit

- Cantaloupe

- Watermelon

- Lemon

Nuts:

- Almonds

- Walnuts

- Cashews nut

- Pistachio

- Macadamia nuts

- Brazil nuts

- Hazelnut

- Pine nuts

- Pecans

Seeds:

- Sesame seeds

- Flax seeds

- Chia seeds

- Hemp seeds

- Pumpkin seeds

Cheese:

- Cheddar cheese, full-fat, organic

- Blue cheese, full-fat, organic

- Feta cheese, full-fat, organic

- Parmesan cheese, full-fat, organic

- Mozzarella cheese, full-fat, organic

Sweeteners:

- Stevia

- Erythritol

- Xylitol

- Swerve

Sauces:

- Guacamole

- Butter sauce

- Mayonnaise, full-fat, organic

- Tomato sauce with no sugar

Drinks:

- Almond milk, unsweetened

- Coconut milk, unsweetened

- Hemp seed milk, unsweetened

- Bone broth

- Plain tea, unsweetened

- Green tea

- Black coffee, unsweetened with moderation

Spices:

- Almost all of them can be used in a small amount

Chapter 3: Foods to Avoid

There are many foods that you need to avoid on the keto diet in order to initiate the ketogenic diet.

Protein:

- Cold cuts with sugar
- Preserve meat especially in sugar solutions
- Nuggets
- Processed meat products

Fat:

- Margarine
- Artificial Trans fat
- Deep-fried foods
- Fast foods

Vegetables:

- Potatoes
- Corn
- Raisins
- All vegetables that grow in the ground and high in carb

Nuts:

- Sweetened nut butter
- Trail mixes with dried fruits
- Chocolate nuts

Dairy:

- Whole milk
- Sweetened Ice cream
- Sweetened yogurt

Sweeteners:

- Honey
- Maple syrup
- White sugar
- Brown sugar

Sauces:

- Barbecue sauce
- High carb tomato ketchup
- Honey mustard sauce

Drinks

- Cold drinks
- Lemonade
- Sweetened fruit juices and smoothies

Chapter 4: FAQs

Question 1

Is the ketogenic diet safe?

Answer

It is not safe for those people who are diagnosed with kidney, pancreas, liver, or gallbladder disease. It also produces a risk of disordered eating in a person. It has many side effects, such as the development of kidney stones, constipation, and diarrhea. If a person drinks enough water and eats a moderate amount of protein, then kidney stones are unlikely.

Question 2

Can keto diet reverse diabetes type 2?

Answer

Unfortunately, it cannot reverse the condition itself but manages the condition significantly. In this diet, both the glucose level and insulin level go down.

Question 3

How much weight can I lose on a keto diet?

Answer

A person can lose over 44 pounds in just 4 months, but it varies from individual to individual.

Question 4

How long do I stay on a keto diet?

Answer

A person should not stay in the state of ketosis for more than 12 weeks because, after a long period, conditions are quite uncertain.

Question 5

What fruits can I eat on a keto diet?

Answer

There are many fruits that you can eat. Strawberries, blackberries, blueberries, raspberries, avocado, and lemon in moderation will be no problem.

Question 6

Should I be concerned about keto flu?

Answer

Unfortunately, yes, you have to be concerned about the keto flu. The keto flu is referred to the drowsiness and fatigue you experience when starting the diet. This is a temporary condition as your body shifts using fats instead of glucose. Once you are used to it, this would not be a problem.

Question 7

How many carbs do I need to take?

Answer

You need to minimize your carbohydrate intake. Eating less than 20 grams of carbohydrate should initiate the process of ketosis.

Question 8

How much protein do I need to take?

Answer

You need to regulate how much protein to eat. Almost 30 to 25% of your daily calories should come from protein. Eat protein in moderation, not too much, because it can hinder the process of ketosis.

Question 9

Can I eat popcorn and other snacks?

Answer

Unfortunately, you cannot eat unnecessary carbohydrates, and that includes popcorn and other snacks. Corn is also a food to avoid in the keto diet.

Chapter 5: 30-Day Meal Plan

Day	Breakfast	Lunch	Dinner	Dessert
1	Bacon and Cheddar Breakfast Casserole	Shrimps and Asparagus	Chicken and Green Beans Skillet	Avocado Ice Cream
2	Bacon and Cheddar Breakfast Casserole	Zucchini Fries	Seared Mustard Lamb Chops	Avocado Ice Cream
3	Mint Chip Smoothie	Taco Chicken Salad	Seared Mustard Lamb Chops	Vanilla and Berry Mug Cake
4	Mushroom Omelet	Taco Chicken Salad	Butter Chicken with Bacon and Spinach	Chocolate Ice Cream
5	Bacon and Egg Quesadilla	Garlic Butter Pork Bites	Butter Chicken with Bacon and Spinach	Chocolate Ice Cream
6	Chocolate and Avocado Smoothie	Lamb Chops	Baked Salmon with Pesto	Cookies
7	Breakfast Hash	Lamb Chops	Baked Salmon with Pesto	Cookies
8	Cheese Omelet	Sausage with Peppers	Chicken Thighs with Creamy Tomato Sauce	Raspberry Ice Cream
9	Green Smoothie	Shrimp Scampi	Chicken Thighs with Creamy Tomato Sauce	Raspberry Ice Cream
10	Bacon and Eggs Plate	Avocado Tuna Bites	Parmesan Cauliflower Rice	Peanut Butter Mousse
11	Frittata	Cheesy Chicken Fritters	Parmesan Cauliflower Rice	Peanut Butter Mousse
12	Frittata	Cheesy Chicken Fritters	Italian Sausage with Cauliflower Rice	Chocolate Cake in a Mug
13	Blueberry Smoothie	Salmon and Avocado Plate	Italian Sausage with Cauliflower Rice	Coconut Ice Cream
14	Broccoli and Cheese Casserole	Avocado and Egg Salad	Creamy Beef with Vegetables	Coconut Ice Cream
15	Broccoli and Cheese Casserole	Shrimp and Bacon Chowder	Creamy Beef with Vegetables	Peanut Butter Mug Cake

16	Breakfast Scramble	Salad in a Jar	Fajita Chicken Casserole	Strawberry Ice Cream
17	Strawberry and Avocado Smoothie	Chicken and Sautéed Zucchini	Fajita Chicken Casserole	Strawberry Ice Cream
18	Caprese Omelet	Chicken and Sautéed Zucchini	Tuna Salad with Eggs	Vanilla and Berry Mug Cake
19	Bacon and Cheddar Breakfast Casserole	Bacon-Wrapped Cheese	Cabbage with Bacon	Chocolate Ice Cream
20	Mint Chip Smoothie	Cheddar Cheese and Bacon Balls	Cabbage with Bacon	Chocolate Ice Cream
21	Mushroom Omelet	Sausage with Lemon Green Beans	Lamb Curry	Cookies
22	Bacon and Egg Quesadilla	Sausage with Lemon Green Beans	Lamb Curry	Cookies
23	Chocolate and Avocado Smoothie	Chicken Thighs with Asparagus	Ground Beef and Green Beans	Raspberry Ice Cream
24	Breakfast Hash	Chicken Thighs with Asparagus	Creamy Salsa Verde Chicken Casserole	Raspberry Ice Cream
25	Cheese Omelet	Asparagus and Salmon Foil Packs	Creamy Salsa Verde Chicken Casserole	Peanut Butter Mousse
26	Green Smoothie	Asparagus and Salmon Foil Packs	Shrimp with Zucchini Noodles	Peanut Butter Mousse
27	Bacon and Eggs Plate	Pork Chops in Mushroom Sauce	Steak with Zucchini Noodles	Chocolate Cake in a Mug
28	Frittata	Pork Chops in Mushroom Sauce	Steak with Zucchini Noodles	Coconut Ice Cream
29	Frittata	Chicken in Creamy Roasted Pepper Sauce	Salmon with Spinach and Tomatoes	Coconut Ice Cream
30	Blueberry Smoothie	Chicken in Creamy Roasted Pepper Sauce	Chicken with Herb Butter	Peanut Butter Mug Cake

Chapter 6: Breakfast

Mushroom Omelet

Preparation time: 5 minutes
Cooking time: 10 minutes
Servings: 1

Ingredients:

- 4 large mushrooms, sliced
- ¼ of medium white onion, chopped
- 1/3 teaspoon ground black pepper
- ½ teaspoon salt
- 2 tablespoons unsalted butter
- 2 tablespoons shredded cheddar cheese
- 3 eggs

Method:

1. Crack eggs in a bowl, add salt and black pepper and whisk until smooth.
2. Take a frying pan, place it over medium heat, add butter and when it melts, add onions and mushrooms and cook for 4 minutes until tender.
3. Pour in the blended egg, cook for 2 to 3 minutes until omelet begins to firm, then top with cheese and fold one half of the omelet to the other.
4. Cook for 3 minutes until the bottom of the omelet has turned golden brown and then slide it to the plate.
5. Serve straight away.

Nutrition Value:

- Calories: 517 Cal
- Fat: 44 g
- Carbs: 6 g
- Protein: 26 g
- Fiber: 1 g
- Net Carb: 5 g

Cheese Omelet

Preparation time: 5 minutes
Cooking time: 5 minutes
Servings: 1

Ingredients:

- ¼ teaspoon salt
- ¼ teaspoon ground black pepper
- 3 tablespoons unsalted butter
- 1/3 cup shredded cheddar cheese
- 3 eggs

Method:

1. Crack eggs in a bowl, add half of the cheese, salt, and black pepper and whisk until smooth.
2. Take a frying pan, place it over medium heat, add butter and when it melts, add mixture and let it cook for 3 minutes until set.
3. Switch heat to medium-low level, continue cooking until omelet is thoroughly cooked, then top with remaining cheese and fold one half of the omelet to the other.
4. Slide omelet to a plate and serve straight away.

Nutrition Value:

- Calories: 448 Cal
- Fat: 40 g
- Carbs: 4 g
- Protein: 9 g
- Fiber: 0 g
- Net Carb: 4 g

Bacon and Eggs Plate

Preparation time: 5 minutes
Cooking time: 5 minutes
Servings: 2

Ingredients:

- 1-ounce arugula lettuce, chopped
- 2 medium avocados, pitted, sliced
- 5 ounces bacon strips
- 1 medium green bell pepper, cored, sliced
- 1/3 teaspoon ground black pepper
- ½ teaspoon salt
- 1 tablespoon chopped chives
- 4 tablespoons chopped walnuts
- 2 tablespoons olive oil
- 4 eggs

Method:

1. Take a frying pan, place it over medium heat and when hot, add bacon strips and cook for 7 to 10 minutes until crispy.
2. Transfer bacon to a plate, keep them warm, then switch heat to medium-low level and fry eggs in it to the desired level.
3. Take two plates, distribute cooked bacon and fried eggs in it, then evenly add bell pepper, lettuce, avocado and nuts, and season with salt and black pepper.
4. Serve straight away.

Nutrition Value:

- Calories: 484 Cal
- Fat: 45 g
- Carbs: 12 g
- Protein: 13 g
- Fiber: 8 g
- Net Carb: 4 g

Caprese Omelet

Preparation time: 5 minutes
Cooking time: 10 minutes
Servings: 4

Ingredients:

- 1.5 ounces cherry tomatoes, halved
- ½ tablespoon dried basil
- ¼ teaspoon ground black pepper
- ¼ teaspoon salt
- 1 tablespoon olive oil
- 3 eggs
- 2.5 ounces mozzarella cheese, sliced

Method:

1. Crack eggs in a bowl, add salt and black pepper, whisk until smooth, and then whisk in basil until mixed.
2. Take a frying pan, place it over medium heat, add oil and when hot, add tomatoes and fry them for 3 minutes.
3. Pour blended eggs on top of tomatoes, cook for 3 minutes until eggs are slightly firm, and sprinkle cheese on top.
4. Switch heat to the low level and cook for 4 minutes until omelet has set.
5. Slide omelet to a plate and serve straight away.

Nutrition Value:

- Calories: 267 Cal
- Fat: 22 g
- Carbs: 2.5 g
- Protein: 16 g
- Fiber: 0.5 g
- Net Carb: 2 g

Bacon and Egg Quesadilla

Preparation time: 5 minutes
Cooking time: 20 minutes
Servings: 2

Ingredients:

- 2 tablespoons diced tomato
- 4 slices of bacon
- 1 tablespoon chopped green onion
- ¾ cup shredded mozzarella cheese
- 3 eggs
- ¾ cup shredded cheddar cheese

Method:

1. Take a pan, place it over medium heat and when hot, add bacon slices and cook them for 5 minutes until crispy, and when done, transfer them to a cutting board and chop them.
2. Crack the eggs, season with salt and black pepper to taste and cook them over medium heat in a pan for 3 to 5 minutes until scrambled to the desired level, set aside until required.
3. Switch on the oven, then set it to 400 degrees F and let it preheat.
4. Place all the cheese in a bowl, stir well, and then spread them on a pizza pan lined with parchment paper; it will make your crust.
5. Bake for 5 minutes, drain excess oil as soon it comes out, top one half of the crust with eggs, bacon, tomato, and green onion and fold the filling with the other half.
6. Press firmly, bake for 5 minutes, and then serve.

Nutrition Value:

- Calories: 150 Cal
- Fat: 8.5 g
- Carbs: 9.5 g
- Protein: 8 g
- Fiber: 1 g
- Net Carb: 8.5 g

Breakfast Hash

Preparation time: 5 minutes
Cooking time: 10 minutes
Servings: 4

Ingredients:

- 3 slices of bacon, chopped
- 1 cup Brussel sprouts, halved
- 1 large turnip, peeled, diced
- 1/4 cup diced red bell pepper
- 1/4 of medium white onion, peeled, diced
- 1/2 teaspoon garlic powder
- 1/2 teaspoon paprika
- 1/2 teaspoon ground black pepper
- 1/2 teaspoon salt
- 1 tablespoon olive oil
- 1 tablespoon parsley

Method:

1. Take a large skillet pan, place it over medium-high heat, add oil and when hot, add turnip, stir in all the spices and cook for 5 minutes.
2. Then add sprouts and onion, continue cooking for 3 minutes until vegetables begin to soften, add chopped bacon along with bell pepper and cook for 7 minutes until bacon has cooked.
3. Garnish hash with parsley and serve straight away.

Nutrition Value:

- Calories: 126 Cal
- Fat: 10 g
- Carbs: 5 g
- Protein: 3 g
- Fiber: 1 g
- Net Carb: 4 g

Frittata

Preparation time: 5 minutes
Cooking time: 30 minutes
Servings: 4

Ingredients:

- 1 cup sliced mushrooms
- 4 ounces baby spinach
- 4 slices of bacon, diced
- 1/2 teaspoon ground black pepper
- 1/2 teaspoon salt
- 2 tablespoons unsalted butter
- 1/4 cup heavy cream
- 1 cup shredded cheddar cheese
- 6 eggs

Method:

1. Switch on the oven, then set it to 355 degrees F and let it preheat.
2. Take a frying pan, place it over medium heat and when hot, add bacon and cook for 4 minutes.
3. Add butter and when it melts, add mushrooms and continue cooking for 3 minutes.
4. Stir in spinach, cook for 2 minutes until the leaves wilt, then remove the pan from heat and sprinkle cheese over vegetables.
5. Crack eggs in a bowl, add black pepper, salt, and cream, whisk until combined, then pour this mixture over the vegetables in the pan and bake for 20 minutes until frittata has cooked and firm.
6. Cut frittata into four slices and then serve straight away.

Nutrition Value:

- Calories: 426 Cal
- Fat: 36 g
- Carbs: 3 g
- Protein: 21 g
- Fiber: 0 g
- Net Carb: 3 g

Bacon and Cheddar Breakfast Casserole

Preparation time: 5 minutes
Cooking time: 25 minutes
Servings: 6

Ingredients:

- 6 slices of bacon, cooked, crumbled
- 3 cups broccoli florets
- 1/2 teaspoon onion powder
- 1/2 teaspoon dried oregano
- 1/2 teaspoon garlic powder
- 1/4 teaspoon ground black pepper
- 1/4 teaspoon dried thyme
- 1/3 teaspoon salt
- 2 tablespoons olive oil
- 4 eggs
- 1 cup shredded cheddar cheese
- 3 tablespoons water
- 1/3 cup heavy whipping cream
- Parsley for garnishing

Method:

1. Switch on the oven, then set it to 350 degrees F and let it preheat.
2. Take a large pan, place it over medium heat and when hot, add florets and winter and cook for 3 minutes until florets have softened and bright green.
3. Remove pan from the heat, drain florets well, transfer them into an 8 by 8-inch casserole dish greased with oil, and then spread them in an even layer.
4. Crack eggs in a bowl, add all the seasoning and cream and whisk until combined.
5. Top florets with cheese and bacon, pour in the egg mixture, and bake for 20 to 23 minutes until the top has golden brown and the casserole has set.
6. When done, let the casserole cool for 10 minutes, then garnish with parsley and serve.

Nutrition Value:

- Calories: 252 Cal
- Fat: 21 g
- Carbs: 4.8 g
- Protein: 13 g
- Fiber: 1.2 g
- Net Carb: 3.6 g

Breakfast Scramble

Preparation time: 5 minutes
Cooking time: 25 minutes
Servings: 2

Ingredients:

- 1 package of frozen cauliflower rice, thawed
- 8 ounces ground turkey
- 1 1/2 large zucchini, diced
- 6 ounces baby spinach
- 1 medium green bell pepper, cored, diced
- ½ of medium red onion, peeled, sliced
- ¾ teaspoon ground black pepper
- ½ teaspoon dried oregano
- ¼ teaspoon cayenne pepper
- 1 teaspoon salt
- 2 eggs, fried
- Avocado oil as needed

Method:

1. Take a bowl, add the turkey in it, add ½ teaspoon salt, cayenne pepper, oregano, and 1/3 teaspoon black pepper, mix until combined, and then shape the mixture into small meatballs.
2. Take a large skillet pan, place it over medium heat, add 2 teaspoon oil and when hot, add meatballs in a single layer and cook for 8 minutes until cooked and golden brown on all sides.
3. Transfer meatballs to a plate, repeat with the remaining balls until cooked, then add 2 teaspoons oil in the pan, and when hot, add bell pepper, zucchini, and onion.
4. Season with ¼ teaspoon each of salt and black pepper, and then cook for 6 minutes until softened.
5. Meanwhile, take a 10-inch skillet pan, place it over medium heat, add 2 teaspoons oil and let it warm.

6. Squeeze moisture from the thawed cauliflower rice, then add into heated pan and season with remaining salt and black pepper.
7. Spread rice with a spatula, let them cook for 5 minutes until golden brown, stir the rice, spread them again, cook for another 5 minutes and then transfer to a plate.
8. Assemble and to do this, place cooked vegetables on top of cauliflower rice, top with meatballs and fried eggs, and then serve.

Nutrition Value:

- Calories: 217.3 Cal
- Fat: 10.2 g
- Carbs: 3.3 g
- Protein: 24.7 g
- Fiber: 0 g
- Net Carb: 3.3 g

Broccoli and Cheese Casserole

Preparation time: 10 minutes
Cooking time: 50 minutes
Servings: 8

Ingredients:

- 1/2 cup sliced green onion
- 6 cups of chopped broccoli
- 1 teaspoon cracked black pepper
- 3 teaspoons all-purpose seasoning blend
- 1/2 cup grated Parmesan Cheese
- 2 cups grated Monterey Jack Cheese
- 14 eggs, beaten
- 2 cups crumbled Feta Cheese

Method:

1. Switch on the oven, then set it to 375 degrees F and let it preheat.
2. Boil broccoli florets in salty water for 4 minutes, then drain them and set aside until required.
3. Crack the eggs in a bowl and then whisk until smooth.
4. Take an 8 by 12 inches casserole dish, grease it with oil, layer the bottom with broccoli and then layer with Monterey Jack Cheese and Feta cheese.
5. Pour egg mixture over cheese layers, use a fork to stir the ingredients gently, and then sprinkle black pepper and all-purpose seasoning blend on top.
6. Then sprinkle with parmesan cheese and onion and bake for 45 minutes until the top has turned golden brown and eggs are firm.
7. Serve straight away.

Nutrition Value:

- Calories: 408 Cal
- Fat: 28 g
- Carbs: 8 g
- Protein: 28 g
- Fiber: 4 g
- Net Carb: 4 g

Strawberry and Avocado Smoothie

Preparation time: 5 minutes
Cooking time: 0 minute
Servings: 5

Ingredients:

- 1 large avocado, pitted, sliced
- 1-pound frozen strawberries
- 1/4 cup erythritol sweetener
- 1 1/2 cup almond milk, unsweetened

Method:

1. Place all the ingredients in the order in a food processor or blender and then pulse for 2 to 3 minutes at high speed until smooth.
2. Pour the smoothie into glasses and then serve straight away.

Nutrition Value:

- Calories: 106 Cal
- Fat: 7 g
- Carbs: 12 g
- Protein: 1 g
- Fiber: 5 g
- Net Carb: 7 g

Blueberry Smoothie

Preparation time: 5 minutes
Cooking time: 0 minute
Servings: 1

Ingredients:

- 1/4 cup blueberries
- 1 teaspoon vanilla extract, unsweetened
- 2 ½ tablespoons protein powder
- 1 teaspoon MCT oil
- 1 cup coconut milk, unsweetened

Method:

1. Place all the ingredients in the order in a food processor or blender and then pulse for 1 minute at high speed until smooth.
2. Pour the smoothie into a glass and then serve straight away.

Nutrition Value:

- Calories: 215 Cal
- Fat: 10 g
- Carbs: 7 g
- Protein: 23 g
- Fiber: 3 g
- Net Carb: 4 g

Green Smoothie

Preparation time: 5 minutes
Cooking time: 0 minute
Servings: 2

Ingredients:

- 2 ounces of cucumber, peeled
- 1/2 of a medium avocado, peeled, pitted
- 1-ounce kale leaves
- 1 stick of celery, chopped
- 1 tablespoon peanut butter
- 2 tablespoons lemon juice
- 1 cup almond milk, unsweetened

Method:

1. Place all the ingredients in the order in a food processor or blender and then pulse for 2 to 3 minutes at high speed until smooth.
2. Pour the smoothie into glasses and then serve straight away.

Nutrition Value:

- Calories: 141 Cal
- Fat: 10.8 g
- Carbs: 8.6 g
- Protein: 4 g
- Fiber: 3.8 g
- Net Carb: 4.8 g

Chocolate and Avocado Smoothie

Preparation time: 5 minutes
Cooking time: 0 minute
Servings: 1

Ingredients:

- 1 teaspoon hemp powder
- 1/2 of a medium avocado, peeled, pitted
- 1 1/2 tablespoon cocoa powder, unsweetened
- 3 tablespoons erythritol sweetener
- 1 cup vanilla almond milk, unsweetened
- 2/3 cup ice cubes

Method:

1. Place all the ingredients in the order in a food processor or blender and then pulse for 1 minute at high speed until smooth.
2. Pour the smoothie into a glass and then serve straight away.

Nutrition Value:

- Calories: 268 Cal
- Fat: 18.8 g
- Carbs: 6.5 g
- Protein: 9.9 g
- Fiber: 3 g
- Net Carb: 3.5 g

Mint Chip Smoothie

Preparation time: 5 minutes
Cooking time: 0 minute
Servings: 2

Ingredients:

- 1/2 of a medium avocado, peeled, pitted
- 1/2 cup baby spinach leaves
- 3 tablespoons erythritol sweetener
- 1/4 cup mint leaves
- 1 tablespoon cacao nibs and more for serving
- 1/2 cup coconut yogurt
- 1 cup coconut milk, unsweetened
- 1 cup ice

Method:

1. Place all the ingredients in the order in a food processor or blender and then pulse for 2 to 3 minutes at high speed until smooth.
2. Pour the smoothie into glasses, top with some more cocoa nibs and then serve straight away.

Nutrition Value:

- Calories: 303 Cal
- Fat: 26.4 g
- Carbs: 12.2 g
- Protein: 2.4 g
- Fiber: 4.2 g
- Net Carb: 8 g

Chapter 7: Appetizers and Snacks

Deviled Eggs

Preparation time: 5 minutes
Cooking time: 0 minute
Servings: 4

Ingredients:

- 8 shrimp, peeled, deveined, cooked
- 1/8 teaspoon herbal salt
- 1 teaspoon tabasco
- ¼ cup mayonnaise
- 4 eggs, boiled
- Chopped dill for garnish

Method:

1. Boil the eggs until firm, then cool and peel them, and cut each egg in half.
2. Scoop the egg yolks into a bowl, mash with a fork and then stir in salt, mayonnaise, and tabasco sauce until mixed.
3. Spoon this mixture into hollows of egg whites, then top with shrimps and sprinkle with dill.
4. Serve straight away.

Nutrition Value:

- Calories: 163 Cal
- Fat: 15 g
- Carbs: 0.5 g
- Protein: 7 g
- Fiber: 0 g
- Net Carb: 0.5 g

Peanut Butter Balls

Preparation time: 40 minutes
Cooking time: 0 minute
Servings: 40

Ingredients:

- 3/4 cup coconut flour
- ½ cup monk fruit sweetener
- 2 cups peanut butter

Method:

1. Take a medium bowl, place all the ingredients in it, and stir well until thick batter comes together.
2. Shape the mixture into small bowls, then place them on a baking tray lined with parchment paper and refrigerate them for 30 minutes.
3. Serve straight away.

Nutrition Value:

- Calories: 57 Cal
- Fat: 4 g
- Carbs: 3 g
- Protein: 0 g
- Fiber: 1.5 g
- Net Carb: 1.5 g

Nut Bars

Preparation time: 65 minutes
Cooking time: 1 minute
Servings: 10

Ingredients:

- 1 cup mixed seeds
- 1 tablespoon chia seeds
- 1/2 cup shredded coconut
- 1 cup mixed nuts, chopped
- 1/4 teaspoon salt
- 1 teaspoon vanilla extract, unsweetened
- 1/3 cup Fiber Syrup
- 2 tablespoons coconut oil
- 3 tablespoons peanut butter

Method:

1. Take a heatproof bowl, place butter, oil, and fiber syrup in it, stir until mixed and microwave for 30 seconds.
2. Meanwhile, take a bowl, add nuts, seeds, and remaining ingredients in it and stir until mixed.
3. Pour in melted butter mixture and then stir until thoroughly combined.
4. Take an 8 by 8 inches baking tin, line it with baking paper, add prepared nut mixture in it, and spread it evenly with the back of a cup.
5. Freeze the nut mixture for 1 hour, then cut it into ten bars and serve.

Nutrition Value:

- Calories: 268 Cal
- Fat: 22 g
- Carbs: 15 g
- Protein: 7 g
- Fiber: 11 g
- Net Carb: 11 g

Fat Bombs

Preparation time: 2 hours and 5 minutes
Cooking time: 0 minute
Servings: 4

Ingredients:

- 1/4 cup cacao powder
- 1 tablespoon stevia
- 1/8 teaspoon salt
- 1/4 cup melted coconut oil
- 1/2 cup coconut butter

Method:

1. Take a large bowl, place all the ingredients in it, and stir until smooth.
2. Spoon the mixture into ice cube trays and freeze for 1 to 2 hours until set.
3. Serve straight away.

Nutrition Value:

- Calories: 84 Cal
- Fat: 8.2 g
- Carbs: 2.6 g
- Protein: 2 g
- Fiber: 1 g
- Net Carb: 1.6 g

Candied Pecans

Preparation time: 5 minutes
Cooking time: 11 minutes
Servings: 32

Ingredients:

- 4 cups pecans, unsalted
- 1/4 teaspoon cayenne pepper
- 1/2 cup erythritol sweetener
- 1 teaspoon salt
- 1 teaspoon cinnamon
- 1 teaspoon vanilla extract, unsweetened
- 1/2 cup butter, unsalted

Method:

1. Switch on the oven, then set it to 325 degrees F and let it preheat.
2. Take a heatproof bowl, add butter in it, and microwave for 30 seconds or more until it melts.
3. Stir in salt, cayenne pepper, cinnamon, erythritol, and vanilla until combined and then mix pecans in it.
4. Take a baking sheet, line it with parchment paper, spread the pecan mixture in it evenly, and then bake for 10 minutes.
5. When done, let nuts cool completely and then serve straight away.

Nutrition Value:

- Calories: 101 Cal
- Fat: 10 g
- Carbs: 2.2 g
- Protein: 1.5 g
- Fiber: 1.6 g
- Net Carb: 0.6 g

Pepperoni Chips

Preparation time: 5 minutes
Cooking time: 7 minutes
Servings: 6

Ingredients:

- 5 ounces pepperoni slices, uncured

Method:

1. Switch on the oven, then set it to 400 degrees F and let it preheat.
2. Take a large baking sheet, place a cookie rack on it, arrange pepperoni slices on it, and bake for 5 to 7 minutes until slices turn crispy.
3. When done, cool the pepperoni slices and then serve straight away.

Nutrition Value:

- Calories: 116 Cal
- Fat: 10 g
- Carbs: 0 g
- Protein: 5 g
- Fiber: 0 g
- Net Carb: 0 g

Lemon and Garlic Zucchini Noodles

Preparation time: 5 minutes
Cooking time: 5 minutes
Servings: 2

Ingredients:

- 4 medium zucchinis
- 1 cup chopped cilantro
- 2 teaspoons minced garlic
- 1/2 teaspoon red chili pepper flakes
- 1/2 of lemon, juiced
- 1 tablespoon hot sauce
- 2 tablespoons butter, unsalted

Method:

1. Prepare zucchini noodles, and for this, spiralized the zucchini into noodles by using a vegetable peeler or spiralizer.
2. Take a skillet pan, place it over medium heat, add butter and when it melts, stir in half of the cilantro, red pepper, garlic, lemon juice, and hot sauce, then toss zucchini noodles until coated and cook for 4 minutes until noodles are tender-crisp.
3. Serve straight away.

Nutrition Value:

- Calories: 625 Cal
- Fat: 50 g
- Carbs: 2 g
- Protein: 39 g
- Fiber: 0.2 g
- Net Carb: 1.4 g

Chili Cheese Bites

Preparation time: 1 hour and 10 minutes
Cooking time: 0 minute
Servings: 4

Ingredients:

- 6 slices of bacon, cooked, chopped
- 1 green onion, sliced
- 1 teaspoon garlic powder
- 1 1/2 teaspoon red chili powder, divided
- 1 teaspoon hot sauce
- 1/4 teaspoon salt
- 1/2 teaspoon paprika
- 1 teaspoon Worcestershire sauce
- 4 cups shredded Colby Jack cheese
- 8 ounces cream cheese, softened

Method:

1. Take a bowl, place all the ingredients in it, except for bacon and ½ teaspoon red chili powder and stir until combined.
2. Take a shallow dish, place chopped bacon in it and then sprinkle with remaining red chili powder.
3. Shape the prepared mixture into 1-inch balls, then press them into bacon mixture until coated and refrigerate for 1 hour.
4. Serve straight away.

Nutrition Value:

- Calories: 81 Cal
- Fat: 6 g
- Carbs: 0 g
- Protein: 3 g
- Fiber: 0 g
- Net Carb: 0 g

Cauliflower and Bacon Dip

Preparation time: 10 minutes
Cooking time: 50 minutes
Servings: 20

Ingredients:

- 4 slices of bacon, cooked, crumbled
- 1-pound cauliflower florets
- ¼ cup chopped chives
- 2 cloves of garlic, peeled
- 2/3 teaspoon ground black pepper
- 1 1/3 teaspoon salt
- 1 tablespoon avocado oil
- 2 cups grated cheddar cheese and more for topping
- 1 cup sour cream
- 1 tablespoon chopped red onion, garnish

Method:

1. Switch on the oven, then set it to 425 degrees F and let it preheat.
2. Meanwhile, place florets in a bowl, season with salt and black pepper, drizzle with oil and toss until well coated.
3. Spread florets in a baking dish, then roast them for 25 minutes, stirring halfway, and when done, bring florets to the room temperature.
4. Then transfer florets in a food processor, add remaining ingredients except for red onion and pulse for 2 minutes until smooth.
5. Tip the mixture in a baking dish, sprinkle with some more cheese, and then bake for 25 minutes until cheese has melted and golden brown.
6. When done, garnish the dip with red onions and then serve with vegetable sticks.

Nutrition Value:

- Calories: 80 Cal
- Fat: 7 g
- Carbs: 2 g
- Protein: 3 g
- Fiber: 0.5 g
- Net Carb: 1.5 g

Spinach Balls

Preparation time: 5 minutes
Cooking time: 10 minutes
Servings: 22

Ingredients:

- 1 cup almond flour
- 2/3 cup cooked spinach, chopped
- 1/4 cup chopped parsley
- 2 tablespoon ground psyllium husk
- 1 teaspoon garlic powder
- 1 teaspoon salt
- 1 cup grated mozzarella cheese
- 3 eggs, beaten

Method:

1. Switch on the oven, then set it to 370 degrees F and let it preheat.
2. Meanwhile, take a large bowl, place chopped spinach in it, add remaining ingredients and stir until batter comes together.
3. Shape the mixture into twenty-two balls, roll them in almond flour, then place them on a cookie tray lined with baking paper and bake them for 30 minutes until the top has turned golden.
4. Serve straight away.

Nutrition Value:

- Calories: 49 Cal
- Fat: 1.9 g
- Carbs: 1.2 g
- Protein: 3.4 g
- Fiber: 0.8 g
- Net Carb: 0.4 g

Shrimp Wrapped in Bacon

Preparation time: 15 minutes
Cooking time: 15 minutes
Servings: 4

Ingredients:

- 1-pound large shrimp, peeled, deveined, butterflied
- 6 strips of bacon
- 1 tablespoon minced garlic
- 1/4 teaspoon turmeric
- 1/2 teaspoon smoked paprika
- 1/4 teaspoon sea salt
- 1/4 cup basil
- 2 tablespoons avocado oil

Method:

1. Switch on the oven, then set it to 400 degrees F and let it preheat.
2. Meanwhile, place shrimps in a plastic bag, add garlic and oil, seal the bag, shake to coat the shrimps with garlic and oil, and let them marinate for 5 minutes.
3. While shrimps marinate, place basil in a food processor, add salt, paprika, and turmeric and pulse for 1 minute until blended.
4. When shrimps are marinated, stuff prepared basil mixture into each shrimp and then fold shrimps back together.
5. Cut each strip of bacon lengthwise, then cut the strip in half, then wrap each stuffed shrimp with a bacon strip, secure with a toothpick if needed.
6. Place wrapped shrimps on a sheet pan, bake them for 15 minutes until bacon crisps and shrimps turn pink.
7. Serve straight away.

Nutrition Value:

- Calories: 200.5 Cal
- Fat: 12.1 g
- Carbs: 2.1 g
- Protein: 19.7 g
- Fiber: 0.4 g
- Net Carb: 1.7 g

Chocolate Covered Bacon

Preparation time: 40 minutes
Cooking time: 10 minutes
Servings: 2

Ingredients:

- 4 slices of bacon, organic, halved
- 1/8 teaspoon sea salt
- ½ block of chocolate fuel bar, melted

Method:

1. Switch on the oven, then set it to 350 degrees F and let it preheat.
2. Then take a baking tray, line it with baking paper, place bacon slices on it in a single layer and bake for 5 to 10 minutes until crispy.
3. Meanwhile, place chocolate in a heatproof bowl and microwave for 30 seconds or more until it melts.
4. When the bacon has baked, drain excess fat from the bacon, pat dry with paper towels and dip bacon with melted chocolate until half-covered.
5. Place chocolate-covered bacon on a plate lined with baking paper and freeze for 30 minutes until firm.
6. Serve straight away.

Nutrition Value:

- Calories: 370 Cal
- Fat: 28 g
- Carbs: 11 g
- Protein: 15 g
- Fiber: 3 g
- Net Carb: 8 g

Chapter 8: Beef, Pork, and Lamb

Lamb Chops

Preparation time: 5 minutes
Cooking time: 10 minutes
Servings: 4

Ingredients:

- 8 lamb chops
- 1 teaspoon ground black pepper
- 1 ½ teaspoon salt
- 1 tablespoon olive oil
- 1 tablespoon unsalted butter
- For Serving:
- 1 lemon, cut into wedges
- ½ cup herb butter

Method:

1. Bring lamb chops to room temperature, remove excess fat and then season with salt and black pepper.
2. Take a frying pan, place it over medium heat, add oil and butter and when the butter melts, add lamb chops in the single layer and fry them for 4 minutes per side until cooked to the desired level.
3. Transfer fried lamb chops to a plate and then repeat with the remaining lamb chops.
4. Serve lamb chops with herb butter and lemon wedges.

Nutrition Value:

- Calories: 90.3 Cal
- Fat: 7.75 g
- Carbs: 0 g
- Protein: 5.3 g
- Fiber: 0 g
- Net Carb: 0 g

Seared Mustard Lamb Chops

Preparation time: 10 minutes
Cooking time: 20 minutes
Servings: 4

Ingredients:

For the Lamb Chops:

- 6 lamb chops, fat trimmed
- 1 teaspoon minced garlic
- 2/3 teaspoon ground black pepper
- 1 tablespoon minced rosemary
- 1 teaspoon salt
- 2 tablespoons olive oil

For the Mustard Sauce:

- 1 sprig of rosemary
- 1 tablespoon mustard powder
- 1 tablespoon minced shallot,
- 1 sprig of thyme
- 2 teaspoons lemon juice
- 1 teaspoon erythritol sweetener
- ½ teaspoon ground black pepper
- ½ teaspoon salt
- 2 teaspoons Worcestershire sauce
- 2 tablespoons unsalted butter
- 1/2 cup beef broth,
- 2/3 cup heavy cream
- 2 tablespoons Brandy

Method:

1. Prepare lamb chops, place them in a baking dish, and season with salt and black pepper.

2. Stir together rosemary, garlic, and oil, then brush this mixture on both sides of lamb chops, cover them with a plastic wrap and marinate overnight in the refrigerator.
3. When ready to cook, bring lamb chops to room temperature, then heat a frying pan over medium-high heat, add 1 tablespoon oil and when hot, switch heat to medium level, add marinated lamb chops in the single layer and cook for 7 minutes per side until chops have cooked to the desired level.
4. When done, wrap lamb chops in a foil and repeat with the remaining lamb chops with remaining oil.
5. Prepare the sauce and for this, take a saucepan, place it over medium-low heat, add shallots, drizzle some water and cook for 5 minutes until softened.
6. Then pour in brandy and beef broth, switch heat to medium, then simmer the sauce for 1 minute and whisk in sweetener, mustard, and Worcestershire sauce until combined.
7. Then add a sprig of thyme and rosemary, whisk in cream and simmer the sauce for 8 minutes until it has thickened to the desired level.
8. Whisk in butter and lemon juice and simmer the sauce more for 3 minutes until sauce is glossy.
9. When done, remove sprigs of herbs from the sauce, then drizzle it over lamb chops and serve.

Nutrition Value:

- Calories: 426 Cal
- Fat: 30 g
- Carbs: 4 g
- Protein: 31 g
- Fiber: 1 g
- Net Carb: 3 g

Lamb Curry

Preparation time: 15 minutes
Cooking time: 1 hour and 20 minutes
Servings: 14

Ingredients:

For Marinade:

- 1 teaspoon onion powder
- 1 ½ teaspoon minced garlic
- 2 teaspoons chopped ginger
- 1 teaspoon ground turmeric
- 2 teaspoons ground cumin
- 1 teaspoon red chili powder
- 2 teaspoons ground coriander
- 1 teaspoon ground cardamom
- 2 tablespoons olive oil
- 1 teaspoon ground paprika

For Curry:

- 1 medium white onion, peeled, diced
- 4 pounds lamb shoulder, diced
- 1/2 cup flaked almonds
- 1 teaspoon ground black pepper
- 2 teaspoons salt
- 1 teaspoon red chili powder
- 1 teaspoon ground cinnamon
- 1 cup heavy cream
- 3 tablespoons clarified butter, organic
- 3 tablespoons chopped cilantro

Method:

1. Prepare the marinade and for this, take a large bowl, place all its ingredients in it and whisk until combined.
2. Then add lamb, toss until well coated and marinate for a minimum of 1 hour in the refrigerator.
3. When ready to cook, take a large saucepan, place it over medium heat, add butter and when it melts, add onion, stir in red chili powder and cinnamon and cook for 3 minutes.
4. Then add marinated lamb, season with salt and black pepper, stir well, cook for 10 minutes, and stir in cream.
5. Switch heat to the low level, and then simmer the curry for 1 hour until meat is tender, partially cover the pan.
6. Then uncover the pan, continue simmering the curry for 10 minutes, stir in almonds, and taste to adjust seasoning.
7. Garnish the curry with cilantro and serve straight away.

Nutrition Value:

- Calories: 480 Cal
- Fat: 38 g
- Carbs: 2 g
- Protein: 30 g
- Fiber: 1 g
- Net Carb: 1 g

Garlic Butter Pork Bites

Preparation time: 10 minutes
Cooking time: 20 minutes
Servings: 4

Ingredients:

- 1-pound green beans, trimmed, blanched
- 1 ½ pound pork chops
- 1/2 of lemon, juiced
- 2 teaspoons minced garlic
- 1 tablespoon Cajun seasoning
- ½ teaspoon red chili pepper flakes
- 1/4 cup unsalted butter
- 2 tablespoons olive oil, divided
- 1/4 cup vegetable broth
- 2 tablespoons chopped parsley
- Lemon slices as needed for the garnish

Method:

1. Cut pork into 1-inch cubes, then place them in a large bowl, sprinkle with Cajun seasoning and toss to coat.
2. Then take a skillet pan, place it over medium-high heat, add oil and when hot, add seasoned pork cubes and cook for 3 minutes per side until seared.
3. When done, transfer pork cubes to a plate, switch heat to medium level, add butter into the pan and when it melts, add garlic and cook for 1 minute until fragrant.
4. Stir lemon juice and vegetable to remove browned bits from the bottom of the pot, cook for 2 minutes, add beans, toss until mixed and cook them for 4 minutes.
5. Then push the beans to one side of the pan, place pork bites to the empty side of the pan, and toss the pork to coat with the sauce.
6. Garnish with parsley and serve pork and green beans with lemon slices.

Nutrition Value:

- Calories: 453 Cal
- Fat: 26 g
- Carbs: 16.3 g
- Protein: 40 g
- Fiber: 4.5 g
- Net Carb: 11.8 g

Pork Chops in Mushroom Sauce

Preparation time: 5 minutes
Cooking time: 15 minutes
Servings: 4

Ingredients:

- 4 pork chops, bone-in, each about 1-inch thick
- 1 teaspoon garlic powder
- ¾ teaspoon ground black pepper
- 1 ½ teaspoon salt
- 1 teaspoon paprika
- 2 tablespoons olive oil
- 2 tablespoons unsalted butter

For the Mushroom Sauce:

- 2 teaspoons minced garlic
- 1 cup sliced brown mushrooms
- 1 tablespoon chopped parsley
- ½ teaspoon ground black pepper
- 1 2/3 teaspoon salt
- 1 teaspoon Italian seasoning
- 1 tablespoon olive oil
- 1/2 cup chicken broth
- 1 1/2 cups heavy cream

Method:

1. Prepare the chops and for this, mix together garlic powder, black pepper, salt, and paprika and sprinkle this spice-mix on both sides of pork chops until coated.
2. Take a skillet pan, place it over medium-high heat, add oil and butter and when the butter melts, add pork chops and sear them for 5 minutes per side or until browned and cooked to the desired level.
3. When done, transfer pork chops to a plate, cover with foil to keep them warm, and set aside until required.

4. Prepare the sauce and for this, add oil in the skillet pan, and when hot, add mushrooms and stir0fry them for 3 minutes until golden brown.
5. Stir in parsley and garlic, season with Italian seasoning, cook for 30 seconds, and pour in broth and stir in cream.
6. Simmer the sauce for 4 minutes until it has thickened slightly, then add pork chops and continue simmering for 3 minutes until chops are cooked to the desired level.
7. Garnish chops with some more parsley and serve them with zucchini noodles.

Nutrition Value:

- Calories: 573.8 Cal
- Fat: 41 g
- Carbs: 7.3 g
- Protein: 44.2 g
- Fiber: 1 g
- Net Carb: 6.3 g

Ground Beef and Green Beans

Preparation time: 5 minutes
Cooking time: 10 minutes
Servings: 2

Ingredients:

- 9 ounces green beans, trimmed
- 10 ounces ground beef
- 1/3 teaspoon ground black pepper
- ½ teaspoon salt
- 3.5 ounces unsalted butter
- 1/3 cup mayonnaise

Method:

1. Take a frying pan, place it over high heat, add half of the butter and when it melts, add beef and cook for 3 to 5 minutes until browned and cooked.
2. Season beef with salt and black pepper, switch heat to medium level, add remaining butter and green beans, toss until mixed, and cook for 5 minutes.
3. Taste to adjust seasoning and then serve beef and green beans with mayonnaise.
4. Serve straight away.

Nutrition Value:

- Calories: 347 Cal
- Fat: 30 g
- Carbs: 4 g
- Protein: 16 g
- Fiber: 1.5 g
- Net Carb: 2.5 g

Italian Sausage with Cauliflower Rice

Preparation time: 5 minutes
Cooking time: 20 minutes
Servings: 2

Ingredients:

- 1/2 head of cauliflower, riced
- 4 Italian sausages
- 1 ½ teaspoon minced garlic
- 1/2 lime, zested
- 1 tablespoon chopped cilantro
- 1/3 teaspoon ground black pepper
- 1 teaspoon Italian seasoning
- 1 tablespoon Sriracha sauce
- 1 tablespoon avocado oil
- 2 tablespoons lime juice
- 1/4 cup chicken stock
- ¼ cup of water

Method:

1. Take a skillet pan, place it over medium-low heat, pour in water, bring it to a boil, then add sausage and let them cook until done, turning frequently and covering the pan with the lid.
2. Then uncover the pan and continue cooking until all the liquid evaporates, and sausages are nicely browned on all sides, turning frequently.
3. When done, transfer sausages to a plate, set them aside, then add oil in the pan, and when hot, add garlic and cook for 1 minute until fragrant.
4. Stir in cauliflower rice, sprinkle with Italian seasoning, drizzle with Sriracha sauce and lime juice, pour in the broth, and simmer for 4 minutes.
5. Stir in cilantro and lime zest, season with black pepper, then return sausages into the pan and cook for 2 minutes until hot.
6. Serve straight away.

Nutrition Value:

- Calories: 255 Cal
- Fat: 12.8 g
- Carbs: 8.5 g
- Protein: 25.5 g
- Fiber: 2.6 g
- Net Carb: 5.9 g

Steak with Zucchini Noodles

Preparation time: 10 minutes
Cooking time: 15 minutes
Servings: 4

Ingredients:

- 4 medium zucchinis
- 1 1/2-pound steak, sliced
- 2 teaspoons minced garlic
- 1/4 cup chopped parsley
- 1/4 teaspoon crushed red pepper flakes
- ½ teaspoon ground black pepper
- 1 teaspoon salt
- 2 tablespoons avocado oil
- 2 tablespoons clarified butter, organic
- 1 lemon, juiced, zested
- 1/4 cup chicken broth

For the Marinade:

- 1/4 cup lemon juice
- 1/3 cup soy sauce
- 1 tablespoon Sriracha sauce
- 1/2 cup avocado oil

Method:

1. Whisk together all the ingredients for the steak marinade in a bowl, pour it into a plastic bag, add steak slices, seal the bag, shake to coat them, and let the steak pieces marinate in the refrigerator for 30 minutes.
2. Meanwhile, prepare zucchini noodles and, for this, spiralized the zucchini into noodles by using a vegetable peeler or spiralizer.
3. When the steak has marinated, bring it to room temperature, take a skillet pan, place it over medium-high heat, add oil and when hot, add steak pieces in a single

layer, season with salt and black pepper and cook for 1 minute, reserving the marinade.

4. Stir in garlic, continue cooking for 2 minutes, and then transfer steaks to a plate, set aside until required.
5. Add butter into the skillet pan, stir in red pepper flakes, lemon juice, and zest, pour in reserved marinade and simmer the sauce for 3 minutes until slightly thickened.
6. Then stir in parsley, toss in zucchini noodles until coated, and cook for 3 to 5 minutes until hot.
7. Return steak pieces, stir well until mixed, and then cook for 1 minute until thoroughly warmed.
8. Serve straight away.

Nutrition Value:

- Calories: 640.6 Cal
- Fat: 44.4 g
- Carbs: 6.5 g

- Protein: 53.7 g
- Fiber: 0.5 g
- Net Carb: 6 g

Creamy Beef with Vegetables

Preparation time: 10 minutes
Cooking time: 20 minutes
Servings: 4

Ingredients:

- 2 cups sliced mushrooms
- 1 medium white onion, peeled, sliced
- 1 1/2-pound steak, diced
- 1 cup broccoli florets
- 2 teaspoons minced garlic
- 1 pouch of onion gravy, keto
- ½ teaspoon ground black pepper
- 1 cup beef stock
- 2 tablespoons unsalted butter
- 4 ounces cream cheese

For Cauliflower Puree:

- 1/2 cup water
- 1 large head of cauliflower, riced

Method:

1. Switch on the instant pot, press the sauté button and when hot, add butter and when it melts, add steak pieces and cook for 3 minutes per side.
2. Add all the vegetables along with garlic, stir in salt and black pepper, add cream cheese, and pour in beef stock.
3. Take 1 cup of hot water, stir onion gravy until it dissolves, then pour the mixture over steaks and vegetables and shut instant pot with the lid, in the sealed position.
4. Press the "meat/stew" button, cook for 20 minutes on high-pressure settings and, when done, do quick pressure release.
5. While steak and vegetable cooks, prepare the cauliflower rice, and for this, place the cauliflower rice in a shallow dish, pour in water, cover the dish, and microwave for 7 minutes at high heat setting.

6. Then transfer cauliflower in a food processor and then pulse for 2 minutes until smooth.
7. Serve the stew with cauliflower.

Nutrition Value:

- Calories: 548 Cal
- Fat: 38.2 g
- Carbs: 13 g

- Protein: 39.1 g
- Fiber: 2.5 g
- Net Carb: 10.5 g

Sausage with Lemon Green Beans

Preparation time: 10 minutes
Cooking time: 15 minutes
Servings: 4

Ingredients:

- 1-pound green beans, trimmed
- 1-pound Italian sausage
- 1 tablespoon thyme leaves
- 3 teaspoons minced garlic
- 1/2 cup chopped parsley
- 2/3 teaspoon ground black pepper
- 1 teaspoon salt
- 1 teaspoon Italian seasoning
- 1 teaspoon red pepper flakes
- 1 tablespoon Sriracha sauce
- ½ of lemon, juiced
- ½ of lemon, sliced
- 3 tablespoons unsalted butter, divided
- 1/4 cup beef stock, pastured
- 1 cup water, divided

Method:

1. Take a heatproof bowl, place green beans in it, pour in ½ cup water and microwave for 10 minutes until tender-crisp.
2. Meanwhile, take a skillet pan, place it over medium heat, arrange sausages in it, pour in remaining water and cook for 10 minutes, turning frequently and covering the pan.
3. Then uncover the pan, continue cooking until water has evaporated completely, add half of the garlic and 3 tablespoons butter, stir in half of the red pepper flakes and cook for 3 minutes until sausage has browned on all sides.

4. Transfer sausage to a plate, switch heat to the low level, add remaining butter and when it melts, add green beans and remaining garlic, stir in remaining ingredients and cook for 3 minutes until the sauce has thickened.

5. Return sausage into the pan, toss well, taste to adjust seasoning and cook for 2 minutes until hot.

6. Serve straight away.

Nutrition Value:

- Calories: 528 Cal
- Fat: 43 g
- Carbs: 19.1 g

- Protein: 19.4 g
- Fiber: 4.8 g
- Net Carb: 14.3 g

Steak Kebabs

Preparation time: 15 minutes
Cooking time: 15 minutes
Servings: 2

Ingredients:

- 8 ounces steak
- 1/2 of red onion, peeled, diced
- 1 medium yellow bell pepper, diced
- 2 tablespoons chopped parsley

For the Marinade:

- 1 ½ teaspoon minced garlic
- ½ teaspoon ground black pepper
- 1 teaspoon garlic powder
- 1/4 cup soy sauce
- 1 tablespoon Sriracha sauce
- 1 lime, juiced
- 2 tablespoons avocado oil

Method:

1. Prepare the marinade and for this, place all of its ingredients in a bowl and whisk until combined.
2. Cut steak into 1-inch pieces, add to the marinade, toss until coated and marinate for a minimum of 2 hours in the refrigerator, stirring halfway.
3. When done, remove steak from the marinade and then thread the steaks pieces into soaked wooden skewers alternating with onion and bell pepper slices.
4. Preheat the grill, and when hot, place prepared skewers on it and grill for 3 minutes per side until steak pieces have cooked and vegetables are slightly charred.
5. When done, sprinkle parsley over skewers, sprinkle with black pepper and serve skewers with lime slices and cauliflower rice.

Nutrition Value:

- Calories: 562.5 Cal
- Fat: 32.6 g
- Carbs: 12.3 g
- Protein: 55.8 g
- Fiber: 0.6 g
- Net Carb: 11.7 g

Sausage with Peppers

Preparation time: 10 minutes
Cooking time: 15 minutes
Servings: 4

Ingredients:

- 6 spicy Italian sausages
- 4 large tomatoes, diced
- 1 medium red bell pepper, sliced
- 1 small red onion, peeled, sliced
- 2 tablespoons crushed tomato
- 2 teaspoons minced garlic
- ½ teaspoon ground black pepper
- 1 teaspoon Italian seasoning
- 1 teaspoon salt
- 1/2 teaspoon crushed chili pepper
- 2 teaspoons crushed fennel seeds
- 2 tablespoons avocado oil
- 1/2 cup chicken broth, organic
- 1 scallion, sliced
- 4 tablespoons chopped basil
- ¼ cup of water

Method:

1. Take a large skillet pan, place it over medium heat, add 1 tablespoon oil and when hot, add sausages and cook for 5 minutes until nicely browned on all sides.
2. Pour in water, cook sausages for 7 to 10 minutes until almost cooked, and then transfer them to a cutting board, set aside until required.
3. Add remaining oil into the pan and when hot, add onions, stir in crushed tomatoes, Italian seasoning, red chili flakes, and fennel seeds and cook for 2 minutes.
4. Then add tomatoes and bell peppers, cook for 3 minutes until tender-crisp, season with salt and black pepper, pour in broth and cook for 2 minutes.

5. Cut sausages into ½-inch pieces, add to the pan along with remaining ingredients, except for basil, stir until combined and cook for 10 minutes until the sauce has thickened and sausages are cooked.
6. Garnish sausages with basil and serve straight away.

Nutrition Value:

- Calories: 129 Cal
- Fat: 6.9 g
- Carbs: 12.2 g
- Protein: 6.11 g
- Fiber: 3.5 g
- Net Carb: 8.7 g

Chapter 9: Poultry

Chicken Thighs with Creamy Tomato Sauce

Preparation time: 5 minutes
Cooking time: 20 minutes
Servings: 4

Ingredients:

- 4 large chicken thighs, skinless, boneless
- 1/2 cup sundried tomatoes, chopped
- 1 teaspoon minced garlic
- 1/2 teaspoon ground black pepper
- 1/2 teaspoon salt
- 1 teaspoon Italian seasoning
- 1 teaspoon red pepper flakes
- 1 teaspoon thyme leaves
- 1 tablespoon avocado oil
- 1/2 cup grated parmesan cheese
- 3/4 cup chicken broth
- 1/2 cup heavy cream
- 2 tablespoons chopped Basil

Method:

1. Take a skillet pan, place it over medium-high heat, add oil and when hot, add chicken thighs, sprinkle with Italian seasoning, salt, and black pepper and cook for 5 minutes per side until seared.
2. Then transfer chicken to a plate, switch heat to medium level, add garlic, and cook for 1 minute until fragrant.
3. Stir in cream, red pepper flakes, and thyme, pour in broth and cook for 5 minutes.
4. Stir in cheese and tomatoes, return chicken in the pa, toss to coat chicken in sauce, and continue cooking for 10 minutes.
5. Garnish chicken with basil and serve with cauliflower rice.

Nutrition Value:

- Calories: 513.8 Cal
- Fat: 39.5 g
- Carbs: 4.8 g
- Protein: 33.6 g
- Fiber: 1 g
- Net Carb: 5.8 g

Chicken with Herb Butter

Preparation time: 5 minutes
Cooking time: 10 minutes
Servings: 4

Ingredients:

For the Butter:

- ¼ cup chopped parsley
- ½ teaspoon minced garlic
- ½ teaspoon salt
- 1 teaspoon lemon juice
- ½ teaspoon garlic powder
- 6 ounces unsalted butter, softened, organic

For Chicken:

- 4 chicken breasts
- ½ teaspoon ground black pepper
- 1 teaspoon salt
- 3 tablespoons unsalted butter, organic

Method:

1. Prepare the butter and for this, place all of its ingredients in a small bowl and stir until combined, set aside until required.
2. Prepare chicken and for this, take a frying pan, place it over medium heat, add butter and when it melts, add chicken in it.
3. Season with salt and black pepper and fry the chicken for 7 to 10 minutes until internal temperature reaches 165 degrees F.
4. Transfer chicken to a serving dish, top with prepared herb butter and serve.

Nutrition Value:

- Calories: 224.5 Cal
- Fat: 17.5 g
- Carbs: 1 g
- Protein: 15.7 g
- Fiber: 0.5 g
- Net Carb: 0.5 g

Chicken Thighs with Asparagus

Preparation time: 10 minutes
Cooking time: 25 minutes
Servings: 4

Ingredients:

For the Spice Mix:

- 1/2 teaspoon onion powder
- 2 teaspoons oregano
- 2 teaspoons cumin powder
- 1 teaspoon paprika
- 2 tablespoons avocado oil
- 1/4 cup lemon juice
- 1/4 cup chicken stock

For the Chicken and Asparagus:

- 1-pound asparagus, trimmed
- 1/2 cup chopped parsley
- 4 chicken thighs, skinless, boneless
- 2 teaspoons minced garlic
- ½ teaspoon ground black pepper
- 2/3 teaspoon salt
- ½ teaspoon red chili pepper flakes
- 1 tablespoon avocado oil, divided

Method:

1. Prepare the spice mix and for this, place all of its ingredients in a small bowl and stir until combined.
2. Place chicken in a shallow dish, sprinkle with prepared spice mix until coated on both sides, and let the chicken marinate at room temperature for 30 minutes.
3. Meanwhile, boil asparagus for 2 minutes, then transfer them immediately into the bowl containing ice water and drain them, set aside until required.

4. When the chicken has marinated, take a large skillet pan, place it over medium-low heat, add oil and when hot, place the marinated chicken in it in a single layer and cook for 5 minutes per side until thoroughly cooked, reserving the marinade.

5. Transfer chicken to a plate, set it aside, switch heat to the low level, add garlic and asparagus in the pan along with parsley, stir in pepper flakes and cook for 5 minutes.

6. Pour in reserved marinade, cook for 3 minutes until the sauce has slightly thickened, ten return chicken into the pan and cook for 3 minutes until hot.

7. Taste to adjust seasoning, then garnish chicken and asparagus with parsley and serve.

Nutrition Value:

- Calories: 600 Cal
- Fat: 45 g
- Carbs: 15 g

- Protein: 37 g
- Fiber: 5.4 g
- Net Carb: 9.6 g

Butter Chicken with Bacon and Spinach

Preparation time: 5 minutes
Cooking time: 25 minutes
Servings: 4

Ingredients:

- 6 slices of bacon, cooked, chopped
- 6 chicken thighs, boneless, skinless
- 3 cups baby spinach leaves
- 1 small white onion, peeled, diced
- 3 teaspoons minced garlic
- 2 teaspoons avocado oil
- 2 tablespoons unsalted butter, organic
- 1 3/4 cups half-and-half
- 1/3 cup chicken broth, pastured
- 1 ½ teaspoon salt
- ¾ teaspoon ground black pepper
- 1 teaspoon Italian seasoning
- 1 teaspoon crushed chili pepper flakes
- 1/2 cup grated Parmesan cheese
- 1 teaspoon cornstarch
- 1 tablespoon water

Method:

1. Take a skillet pan, place it over medium heat, add oil and when hot, add chicken thighs, season with salt and black pepper, and cook them for 8 minutes per side until seared.
2. When done, transfer chicken to a plate, set aside until required, then add butter into the pan and when it melts, add onion and garlic and cook for 4 minutes.
3. Stir chicken stock in it, cook for 2 minutes until reduced slightly, then stir bacon in the sauce and cook for 2 minutes.
4. Switch heat to the low level, stir half-and-half, simmer for 3 minutes and then stir in black pepper, salt, and Italian seasoning.

5. Add spinach, stir to coat with sauce, cook for 3 minutes until the leaves wilt, then stir cheese and cook for 3 minutes until cheese melts and the sauce has thickened.
6. Return chicken into the pan, stir to coat them, sprinkle with red pepper flakes and remove the pan from heat.
7. Serve straight away.

Nutrition Value:

- Calories: 1165 Cal
- Fat: 99.2 g
- Carbs: 9.2 g
- Protein: 57.3 g
- Fiber: 2 g
- Net Carb: 7.2 g

Fajita Chicken Casserole

Preparation time: 10 minutes
Cooking time: 20 minutes
Servings: 4

Ingredients:

- 2 large chicken breasts, halved
- 1 medium white onion, peeled, minced
- 2 medium green and red bell peppers, deseeded, cut into strips
- 1 teaspoon garlic powder
- 1 teaspoon cumin powder
- ½ teaspoon ground black pepper
- 1 teaspoon salt
- 1 1/2 teaspoon red chili powder
- 2 teaspoons paprika
- 1 tablespoon avocado oil
- 1 cup shredded Mozzarella cheese
- 2 tablespoons chopped cilantro

Method:

1. Switch on the oven, then set it to 400 degrees F and let it preheat.
2. Place chicken in a shallow dish, sprinkle with all the spices, reserve some of the spices for vegetables, and then arrange chicken into a baking dish greased with oil.
3. Drizzle oil over the chicken, then top with onion and bell pepper, sprinkle remaining spices, and cover chicken and vegetables with cheese.
4. Bake the casserole for 20 minutes until the chicken has cooked, then switch on the broiler and continue cooking for 2 minutes.
5. Serve straight away.

Nutrition Value:

- Calories: 211.3 Cal
- Fat: 12.7 g
- Carbs: 5.5 g
- Protein: 20.3 g
- Fiber: 2.3 g
- Net Carb: 3.2 g

Chicken and Sautéed Zucchini

Preparation time: 10 minutes
Cooking time: 20 minutes
Servings: 4

Ingredients:

- 3 pounds of chicken breast
- 3 medium zucchinis, diced
- 1 ½ teaspoon ground black pepper
- 1/2 teaspoon red chili flakes
- 2 teaspoons salt
- 1 tablespoon avocado oil
- 4 tablespoons chopped parsley

For the Marinade:

- 1/2 teaspoon onion powder
- 4 teaspoons minced garlic
- 2 teaspoons dried oregano
- 1/4 cup avocado oil
- 1 tablespoon smoked paprika
- 1/4 cup lemon juice
- 2 teaspoons cumin powder
- 1/4 cup chicken stock

Method:

1. Take a large bowl, place all the ingredients for the marinade in it, stir until combined, then add chicken, toss to coat them, and marinate for a minimum of 30 minutes in the refrigerator.
2. When the chicken has marinated, take a skillet pan, place it over medium-low heat, add oil and when hot, add chicken pieces and cook for 15 minutes until cooked, reserving the marinade.
3. When done, transfer chicken to a plate, cover with foil to keep chicken warm, and set aside until required.

4. Switch heat to medium-low level, add zucchini into the pan, season with black pepper, chili flakes, and salt and cook for 3 minutes.
5. Then stir the marinade, cook for 4 minutes until the sauce has reduced slightly, and zucchini has turned tender.
6. Distribute zucchini between plats, top with chicken, garnish with parsley, and serve straight away.

Nutrition Value:

- Calories: 693 Cal
- Fat: 40.2 g
- Carbs: 8.7 g

- Protein: 72.5 g
- Fiber: 3.1 g
- Net Carb: 5.6 g

Chicken in Creamy Roasted Pepper Sauce

Preparation time: 5 minutes
Cooking time: 25 minutes
Servings: 4

Ingredients:

- 16 ounces of roasted bell pepper sauce
- 3 medium chicken breasts
- 2 teaspoons Italian seasoning
- 1 teaspoon ground black pepper
- 1 ½ teaspoon salt
- ¼ teaspoon cayenne pepper
- 3 tablespoons avocado oil
- 1/3 cup unsalted butter, diced
- 2 tablespoons grated parmesan cheese and more as needed for garnish
- 2 tablespoons chopped parsley

Method:

1. Take a skillet pan, place it over medium-low heat, add oil and when hot, add chicken in it, sprinkle with black pepper, salt, and Italian seasoning and cook for 5 minutes per side until golden brown.
2. When done, transfer chicken into a plate, switch heat to low, pour in the sauce, and stir in cayenne pepper.
3. Switch heat to medium-low level, simmer sauce to 5 minutes, and then whisk in cheese and butter until melted.
4. Return chicken into the pan, coat with the sauce, and simmer for 3 minutes until hot.
5. Garnish chicken with parsley and serve straight away.

Nutrition Value:

- Calories: 838.5 Cal
- Fat: 48.1 g
- Carbs: 27.5 g
- Protein: 72.8 g
- Fiber: 3.4 g
- Net Carb: 24.1 g

Cheesy Chicken Fritters

Preparation time: 10 minutes
Cooking time: 25 minutes
Servings: 4

Ingredients:

- 3 Jalapeño peppers, deseeded, diced
- 1 ½ pound chicken breast, diced
- 2 tablespoons chopped parsley
- 1 spring onion, sliced and more as needed for garnish
- 1/3 cup almond flour
- 1/2 teaspoon garlic powder
- ½ teaspoon ground black pepper
- 1 teaspoon salt
- 1 tablespoon avocado oil
- 1 cup shredded mozzarella cheese
- 2 eggs
- 1/4 cup grated parmesan cheese

Method:

1. Take a large bowl, place chicken in it, add remaining ingredients except for oil, and stir until combined.
2. Take a skillet pan, place it over medium-low heat, add oil and when hot, add a scoop of chicken mixture in it by using the ice cream scoop, flatten the mixture to make a fritter and cook for 6 minutes per side until thoroughly cooked.
3. When done, transfer fritters to a plate and repeat with the remaining chicken mixture.
4. Serve straight away.

Nutrition Value:

- Calories: 537 Cal
- Fat: 35 g
- Carbs: 5.6 g
- Protein: 49 g
- Fiber: 1.7 g
- Net Carb: 3.9 g

Chicken and Green Beans Skillet

Preparation time: 10 minutes
Cooking time: 20 minutes
Servings: 4

Ingredients:

- 1-pound green beans, trimmed
- 6 chicken thighs, skinless, boneless
- 1/2 cup chopped parsley
- ½ of lemon, juiced
- 2 teaspoons minced garlic
- 1 teaspoon onion powder
- ¼ teaspoon ground black pepper
- ¼ teaspoon salt
- 1 teaspoon paprika
- 1/4 teaspoon crushed red chili pepper flakes
- ½ of lemon, sliced
- 1 tablespoon Sriracha sauce
- 3 tablespoons unsalted butter, divided, organic
- 1/2 cup chicken stock
- ½ cup of water

Method:

1. Prepare the spice mix and for this, stir together black pepper, salt, onion powder, and paprika and then sprinkle this mixture on both sides of the chicken until coated.
2. Take a heatproof bowl, add green beans in it, pour in water and microwave for 8 minutes until tender-crisp.
3. Take a skillet pan, place it over medium-low heat, add 2 tablespoons butter and when it melts, arrange the seasoned chicken in it in a single layer and cook for 6 minutes per side until thoroughly cooked.

4. Transfer chicken to a plate, switch heat to the low level, add remaining butter and when it melts, add green beans, garlic, and parsley, stir in chili pepper flakes and hot sauce and cook for 5 minutes.
5. Stir in lemon juice, pour in the stock and cook for 3 minutes until the sauce has thickened slightly.
6. Then return chicken into the pan, toss until mixed, cook for 2 minutes until hot and then taste to adjust seasoning.
7. Garnish chicken with parsley and serve straight away.

Nutrition Value:

- Calories: 616.6 Cal
- Fat: 45.3 g
- Carbs: 17.6 g
- Protein: 36.6 g
- Fiber: 5.7 g
- Net Carb: 11.9 g

Creamy Salsa Verde Chicken Casserole

Preparation time: 10 minutes
Cooking time: 20 minutes
Servings: 4

Ingredients:

- 4 chicken breasts
- 1 cup salsa verde, keto
- 1/2 teaspoon ground black pepper
- 1/2 teaspoon salt
- 4 ounces shredded Mozzarella cheese
- 8 ounces cream cheese, softened

For Marinade:

- 1 teaspoon garlic powder
- 1/2 teaspoon red pepper flakes
- 1/2 teaspoon ground black pepper
- 1/2 teaspoon salt
- 1/2 teaspoon Italian seasoning
- 1 tablespoon avocado oil

Method:

1. Switch on the oven, then set it to 400 degrees F and let it preheat.
2. Meanwhile, take a plastic bag, add all the ingredients for the marinade in it, seal the bag and shake well until combined.
3. Then add chicken, seal the bag, shake well to coat chicken with the marinade and then arrange them in a baking dish.
4. Spread cheese over the chicken pieces, sprinkle with salt and black pepper, then pour the salsa on top, sprinkle with cheese, and bake for 30 minutes until thoroughly cooked.
5. Serve straight away.

Nutrition Value:

- Calories: 826.3 Cal
- Fat: 56.2 g
- Carbs: 7 g
- Protein: 70.8 g
- Fiber: 0.7 g
- Net Carb: 6.3 g

Chapter 10: Seafood

Salmon and Avocado Plate

Preparation time: 5 minutes
Cooking time: 0 minute
Servings: 1

Ingredients:

- 1 avocado, pitted, sliced
- 3.5 ounces smoked salmon
- 1/8 teaspoon salt
- 1/8 teaspoon ground black pepper
- ¼ cup mayonnaise

Method:

1. Transfer avocado from its shell to a plate, and then add salmon and mayonnaise on the side.
2. Sprinkle with salt and black pepper and then serve straight away.

Nutrition Value:

- Calories: 518.5 Cal
- Fat: 41 g
- Carbs: 8.5 g
- Protein: 32.5 g
- Fiber: 6.5 g
- Net Carb: 2 g

Tuna Salad with Eggs

Preparation time: 5 minutes
Cooking time: 0 minute
Servings: 2

Ingredients:

- 5 ounces tuna, packed in oil
- 4 ounces celery stalks
- 6 ounces chopped Romaine lettuce
- 2 scallions, chopped
- 4 ounces cherry tomatoes
- ½ lemon, zested, juiced
- ¼ teaspoon ground black pepper
- ½ teaspoon salt
- 2 tablespoons avocado oil
- 1 teaspoon Dijon mustard
- ½ cup mayonnaise
- 4 eggs, boiled, peeled, cut into wedges

Method:

1. Take a bowl, place tuna in it, then add mustard, lemon juice and zest, and mayonnaise, season with salt and black pepper, and then stir until combined.
2. Distribute lettuce between two plates, top with tuna mixture, add eggs and tomatoes and then drizzle with oil.
3. Serve straight away.

Nutrition Value:

- Calories: 398 Cal
- Fat: 35 g
- Carbs: 5 g
- Protein: 16.5 g
- Fiber: 2 g
- Net Carb: 3 g

Baked Salmon with Pesto

Preparation time: 5 minutes
Cooking time: 30 minutes
Servings: 4

Ingredients:

For Salmon:

- 4 tablespoons green pesto
- 2/3 teaspoon ground black pepper
- 1 teaspoon salt
- 2 pounds salmon

For Green sauce

- ¼ teaspoon ground black pepper
- 1/3 teaspoon salt
- 1 cup mayonnaise
- 4 tablespoons green pesto
- ½ cup Greek yogurt

Method:

1. Switch on the oven, then set it to 400 degrees F and let it preheat.
2. Meanwhile, take a baking dish, grease it with oil, and place salmon in it, skin-side down.
3. Spread pesto on the top, season with black pepper and salt, and then bake for 30 minutes until fork tender.
4. Meanwhile, prepare the green sauce and for this, place all of its ingredients in a bowl and whisk until combined.
5. Serve straight away.

Nutrition Value:

- Calories: 256 Cal
- Fat: 22 g
- Carbs: 0.7 g
- Protein: 13 g
- Fiber: 0 g
- Net Carb: 0.7 g

Shrimps and Asparagus

Preparation time: 5 minutes
Cooking time: 15 minutes
Servings: 4

Ingredients:

- 1 ½ pound asparagus, trimmed
- 1-pound large shrimp, peeled, deveined
- 1 teaspoon onion powder
- 1 teaspoon cumin
- 1/2 teaspoon garlic powder
- 1/4 teaspoon ground black pepper
- 1 tablespoon red chili powder
- 1 teaspoon salt
- 2 teaspoons paprika
- 1 tablespoon unsalted butter
- 1 tablespoon Sriracha sauce
- 2 tablespoons avocado oil, divided
- 1 tablespoon lemon juice
- 1/4 cup chicken stock
- 2 tablespoons chopped parsley
- Lemon slices as needed for garnish

Method:

1. Take a bowl, add shrimps, sprinkle with onion powder, garlic powder, black pepper, red chili powder, salt, and paprika, stir until well coated and set aside until required.
2. Then take a skillet pan, place it over medium-high heat, add 1 tablespoon oil and when hot, add shrimps and cook for 3 minutes per side until cooked, and when done, transfer shrimps to a plate and set aside until required.
3. Add remaining oil in the skillet pan, add butter, switch heat to medium level, stir in hot sauce, lemon juice and stock and bring the sauce to simmer.

4. Toss the asparagus until coated, continue cooking for 6 minutes until tender-crisp, then push the asparagus to one side of the pan, return shrimps to the empty side of the pan and cook for 2 minutes until hot.

5. Transfer asparagus and shrimps to a dish, garnish with parsley, and then serve with lemon slices and zucchini noodles.

Nutrition Value:

- Calories: 585 Cal
- Fat: 27 g
- Carbs: 20 g
- Protein: 63 g
- Fiber: 14.3 g
- Net Carb: 5.7 g

Salmon with Spinach and Tomatoes

Preparation time: 10 minutes
Cooking time: 20 minutes
Servings: 4

Ingredients:

- 4 salmon fillets
- 5 ounces sun-dried tomato
- 1 small white onion, peeled, diced
- 3 cups baby spinach
- 3 teaspoons minced garlic
- 2/3 teaspoon ground black pepper
- 1 teaspoon salt
- 2 teaspoons avocado oil
- 2 tablespoons unsalted butter
- 1/2 cup grated Parmesan cheese
- 1/3 cup seafood broth
- 1 3/4 cups heavy cream
- 1 tablespoon chopped parsley

Method:

1. Prepare the sauce and for this, take a skillet pan, place it over medium-high heat, add oil and when hot, add salmon seasoned with some salt and black pepper and cook for 5 minutes per side until cooked.
2. When done, transfer salmon to a plate, add butter into the pan and when it melts, add garlic and cook for 1 minute until fragrant.
3. Stir in onion, cook for 4 minutes, then stir in tomatoes and cook for 2 minutes.
4. Switch heat to the low level, pour in broth and cream, stir well and bring the sauce to simmer.
5. Season the sauce with salt and black pepper, add spinach, cook for 3 minutes until leaves wilt, then stir in cheese and simmer sauce for 1 minute until cheese melts.
6. Return salmon into the pan, toss to coat with sauce and garnish with sauce.
7. Serve straight away.

Nutrition Value:

- Calories: 1158 Cal
- Fat: 67.8 g
- Carbs: 17.3 g
- Protein: 117 g
- Fiber: 4 g
- Net Carb: 13.3 g

Asparagus and Salmon Foil Packs

Preparation time: 10 minutes
Cooking time: 12 minutes
Servings: 2

Ingredients:

- 1-pound asparagus, trimmed
- 2 salmon fillets
- 4 teaspoons minced garlic
- 1/3 teaspoon ground black pepper
- 2/3 teaspoon salt
- 1 tablespoon Sriracha sauce
- 1 1/2 tablespoon lemon juice
- 2 tablespoons chicken broth
- 4 tablespoons butter, cubed
- 2 tablespoons chopped parsley

Method:

1. Switch on the oven, then set it to 425 degrees F and let it preheat.
2. Take two 14 by 12 inches sheets of aluminum foil, and then place these pieces on working space.
3. Prepare the sauce, and for this, whisk together Sriracha sauce, lemon juice, and broth until combined.
4. Season salmon with black pepper and salt, place them in the center of the pieces, place asparagus to its side, season more with salt and black pepper and then sprinkle with garlic.
5. Drizzle sauce over salmon and asparagus, scatter butter pieces on top and wrap the packets by crimping the edges, don't wrap tightly.
6. Arrange the packets on the baking sheet and then bake for 12 minutes until salmon has thoroughly.
7. Serve salmon and asparagus with lemon slices.

Nutrition Value:

- Calories: 853 Cal
- Fat: 50 g
- Carbs: 15.4 g
- Protein: 85 g
- Fiber: 5.6 g
- Net Carb: 9.8 g

Shrimp with Zucchini Noodles

Preparation time: 10 minutes
Cooking time: 10 minutes
Servings: 4

Ingredients:

- 4 medium zucchinis
- 1-pound shrimp, peeled, deveined
- 3 teaspoons minced garlic
- 2/3 teaspoon ground black pepper
- 1 ¼ teaspoon salt
- ¼ teaspoon red pepper flakes
- 1 teaspoon Italian seasoning
- ½ of lemon, juiced
- 1 tablespoon Sriracha sauce
- 1 tablespoon avocado oil
- 4 tablespoons unsalted butter, softened, divided
- 1/4 cup chicken stock
- 1/4 cup chopped parsley

Method:

1. Prepare zucchini noodles, and for this, spiralized the zucchini into noodles by using a vegetable peeler or spiralizer.
2. Take a skillet pan, place it over medium-high heat, add oil and half of butter and when hot, add shrimps in a single layer, sprinkle with some salt and black pepper and cook for 1 minute, don't stir.
3. Add garlic, red pepper, and Italian seasoning, stir the shrimps and continue cooking for 2 minutes.
4. Transfer shrimps to a plate, add remaining butter into the pan, and when the butter melts, add lemon juice and Sriracha sauce, pour in the stock, stir well, then bring the sauce to simmer and continue simmering it for 3 minutes.
5. Toss zucchini noodles in the sauce until coated, cook for 2 minutes, then add shrimps, stir until combined and cook for 1 minute until hot.

6. Serve straight away.

Nutrition Value:

- Calories: 250.2 Cal
- Fat: 18.3 g
- Carbs: 3.8 g

- Protein: 17.4 g
- Fiber: 0.5 g
- Net Carb: 3.3 g

Shrimp Scampi

Preparation time: 20 minutes
Cooking time: 10 minutes
Servings: 2

Ingredients:

- 1-pound shrimp, peeled, deveined
- 2 summer squash
- ½ teaspoon minced garlic
- ½ teaspoon ground black pepper
- ¾ teaspoon salt
- 1/8 teaspoon red chili flakes
- 2 tablespoons unsalted butter
- 2 tablespoons lemon juice
- 1/4 cup chicken broth
- 2 tablespoons chopped parsley

Method:

1. Prepare squash noodles and for this, spiralized the squash into noodles by using a vegetable peeler or spiralizer, season with salt, and let stand for 15 minutes.
2. Drain the noodles, pat dry with paper towels and set aside until required.
3. Take a skillet pan, place it over medium heat, add butter and when it melts, stir in garlic and cook for 1 minute until fragrant.
4. Stir in red chili flakes, lemon juice, and chicken broth, bring the sauce to boil, then add shrimps, toss to coat them, switch heat to the low level, and simmer shrimps for 5 minutes until cooked.
5. Taste to adjust seasoning, add noodles and toss until coat.
6. Garnish with parsley and serve straight away.

Nutrition Value:

- Calories: 489 Cal
- Fat: 7.5 g
- Carbs: 8.5 g
- Protein: 48.4 g
- Fiber: 2.4 g
- Net Carb: 5.1 g

Shrimp and Bacon Chowder

Preparation time: 5 minutes
Cooking time: 20 minutes
Servings: 4

Ingredients:

- 1/2 pound of bacon
- 1-pound shrimps, peeled, deveined, chopped
- 1/4 cup chopped white onion
- 2 teaspoons ground black pepper
- 1 ½ teaspoon salt
- 2 teaspoons smoked paprika
- 1 1/2 cups heavy whipping cream
- 3 cups chicken stock

Method:

1. Take a large pot, place it over medium-high heat and when hot, add bacon and cook for 5 minutes until crisp.
2. Transfer bacon to a cutting board, let it cool slightly, then chop it and set aside until required.
3. Add chopped onion into the pot, stir, cook for 4 minutes, then season with black pepper, paprika, and salt, pour in cream and stock, stir until mixed and bring the mixture to a boil.
4. Add shrimps and bacon, switch heat to medium level and simmer for 7 to 10 minutes until shrimps have cooked.
5. Serve straight away.

Nutrition Value:

- Calories: 405 Cal
- Fat: 29 g
- Carbs: 3 g
- Protein: 32 g
- Fiber: 1 g
- Net Carb: 2 g

Avocado Tuna Bites

Preparation time: 10 minutes
Cooking time: 10 minutes
Servings: 4

Ingredients:

- 1 medium avocado, pitted, cubed
- 10 ounces cooked tuna
- 1/3 cup almond flour
- ¼ teaspoon onion powder
- ½ teaspoon garlic powder
- ¼ teaspoon ground black pepper
- ¼ teaspoon salt
- ¼ cup mayonnaise
- ½ cup avocado oil
- ¼ cup grated Parmesan cheese

Method:

1. Take a large bowl, add tuna in it, then add all the spices, cheese, and mayonnaise and stir until combined.
2. Stir avocado cubes until just mixed, then shape the mixture into balls and roll them into almond flour until coated.
3. Take a skillet pan, place it over medium heat, add oil and when hot, add prepared tuna balls and cook for 4 minutes per side until browned on all sides.
4. Serve straight away.

Nutrition Value:

- Calories: 185.2 Cal
- Fat: 17.7 g
- Carbs: 2.1 g
- Protein: 5 g
- Fiber: 1.1 g
- Net Carb: 1 g

Chapter 11: Soups and Sides

Taco Chicken Salad

Preparation time: 15 minutes
Cooking time: 20 minutes
Servings: 4

Ingredients:

For the Chicken:

- 1 teaspoon minced garlic
- 2 chicken breasts
- 2 tablespoons taco seasoning
- 2 tablespoons avocado oil

For the Drizzle:

- ½ lime, juiced
- 1 teaspoon minced garlic
- 1/2 cup cilantro
- ¼ teaspoon ground black pepper
- 1/3 teaspoon salt
- 3 tablespoons avocado oil
- 1/2 cup yogurt

For the Salad:

- 1 medium avocado, peeled, pitted, diced
- 2 heads of lettuce, chopped
- 1/4 cup of diced red onion
- 2 tomatoes, diced
- 2/3 teaspoon ground black pepper

Method:

1. Prepare the chicken and for this, place chicken in a large plastic bag, add remaining ingredients, seal the bag, shake it well to coat chicken with the spice and let it marinate for a minimum of 30 minutes in the refrigerator.
2. When done, preheat the grill over medium-high heat setting and, when hot, add marinated chicken on the grilling rack and cook for 10 minutes per side until thoroughly cooked.
3. When the chicken has cooled, transfer it to a cutting board, let it cool slightly, then cut the chicken into cubes and set aside until required.
4. While chicken grills, prepare the drizzle, and for this, place all of its ingredients in a food processor and pulse doe 2 minutes until smooth.
5. Tip the sauce in a bowl and then set aside in the refrigerator until required.
6. Prepare the salad and for this, take a large salad bowl, place all of the salad vegetables in it, add chicken pieces, sprinkle with black pepper, add prepared drizzle with toss until well mixed.
7. Serve straight away.

Nutrition Value:

- Calories: 512.3 Cal
- Fat: 35.3 g
- Carbs: 20.8 g

- Protein: 32.3 g
- Fiber: 8.2 g
- Net Carb: 11.8 g

Parmesan Cauliflower Rice

Preparation time: 5 minutes
Cooking time: 10 minutes
Servings: 4

Ingredients:

- 1 medium head of cauliflower, grated
- ½ of medium white onion, peeled, chopped
- 2 tablespoons chopped parsley
- 1 teaspoon minced garlic
- 1 teaspoon red chili pepper flakes
- 1 lemon, juiced, zested
- 2 ounces grated parmesan cheese
- 2 tablespoons unsalted butter, divided
- 2 tablespoons vegetable stock

Method:

1. Take a skillet pan, place it over medium heat, add butter and when it melts, add onion and garlic and cook for 1 minute.
2. Then stir in cauliflower rice to coat with butter, cook for 1 minute, then stir in lemon zest, half of parsley and stock, and cook for 1 minute.
3. Stir in lemon juice and cheese, remove the pan from heat, and top with remaining parsley.
4. Serve straight away.

Nutrition Value:

- Calories: 133.5 Cal
- Fat: 10.2 g
- Carbs: 6.1 g
- Protein: 5.6 g
- Fiber: 1.4 g
- Net Carb: 4.7 g

Salad in a Jar

Preparation time: 5 minutes
Cooking time: 0 minute
Servings: 1

Ingredients:

- 4 ounces smoked salmon
- 1 avocado, pitted, chopped
- 1-ounce leafy greens
- 1 medium carrot, shredded
- 1-ounce cherry tomatoes, chopped
- ½ of scallion, sliced
- 1-ounce red bell peppers, chopped
- ¼ cup mayonnaise

Method:

1. Take a salad jar and then place leafy greens in its bottom.
2. Then layer with remaining vegetables, layer tomatoes in the end, and then top with salmon.
3. Spread mayonnaise on top of salmon and serve straight away.

Nutrition Value:

- Calories: 1133 Cal
- Fat: 84 g
- Carbs: 28 g
- Protein: 75 g
- Fiber: 17 g
- Net Carb: 17 g

Bacon-Wrapped Cheese

Preparation time: 5 minutes
Cooking time: 15 minutes
Servings: 2

Ingredients:

- 8 ounces of halloumi cheese
- 6 ounces of bacon, sliced

Method:

1. Switch on the oven, then set it to 450 degrees F and let it preheat.
2. Cut cheese into them slices, and then wrap each slice with a bacon slice.
3. Arrange wrapped cheese on a baking sheet and then bake for 15 minutes until golden brown, flipping halfway.
4. Serve straight away.

Nutrition Value:

- Calories: 176.3 Cal
- Fat: 15.3 g
- Carbs: 1 g
- Protein: 8.5 g
- Fiber: 0 g
- Net Carb: 1 g

Cheddar Cheese and Bacon Balls

Preparation time: 20 minutes
Cooking time: 10 minutes
Servings: 8

Ingredients:

- 5 ounces bacon, sliced
- ½ teaspoon red chili flakes
- ½ teaspoon ground black pepper
- 5 ounces shredded cheddar cheese
- 1 tablespoon unsalted butter, cold
- 2 ounces unsalted butter, softened
- 5 ounces cream cheese

Method:

1. Take a skillet pan, place it over medium heat, add 1 tablespoon butter and when it melts, add bacon slices and cook for 5 to 8 minutes until crisp.
2. Then transfer bacon slices to a cutting board, let them cool slightly, then chop them and transfer in a bowl, set aside until required.
3. Pour bacon grease into the bowl, add remaining ingredients and mix by using an electric hand mixer until combined.
4. Let the mixture chill for 15 minutes until cheese, then shape the mixture into twenty-four balls, and roll the balls into chopped bacon until coated.
5. Serve straight away.

Nutrition Value:

- Calories: 34.3 Cal
- Fat: 3.5 g
- Carbs: 0.25 g
- Protein: 1 g
- Fiber: 0 g
- Net Carb: 0.25 g

Cabbage with Bacon

Preparation time: 5 minutes
Cooking time: 15 minutes
Servings: 2

Ingredients:

- 1 pound of green cabbage, chopped
- 10 ounces of bacon, chopped
- ½ teaspoon ground black pepper
- ½ teaspoon salt
- 2 ounces of unsalted butter

Method:

1. Take a skillet pan, place it over medium heat and when hot, add bacon slices and cook for 7 to 10 minutes until crispy.
2. Then add butter and cabbage, stir well until mixed and cook for 4 minutes until golden brown.
3. Season cabbage and bacon with black pepper and salt and then serve straight away.

Nutrition Value:

- Calories: 425 Cal
- Fat: 39.5 g
- Carbs: 7.5 g
- Protein: 10.5 g
- Fiber: 3 g
- Net Carb: 4.5 g

Roasted Broccoli

Preparation time: 5 minutes
Cooking time: 10 minutes
Servings: 4

Ingredients:

- 1 1/2 pounds of broccoli florets
- 1/2 teaspoon garlic powder
- 1/2 teaspoon salt
- 1 cup grated cheddar cheese

Method:

1. Switch on the oven, then set it to 350 degrees F and let it preheat.
2. Meanwhile, take a heatproof bowl, add broccoli florets in it, and drizzle with 3 tablespoon water and then microwave for 4 minutes until steamed.
3. Spread steamed broccoli on a baking sheet lined with foil, bring the florets together, and season with garlic powder.
4. Sprinkle cheese on top of broccoli and bake for 15 minutes until cheese has melted.
5. Serve straight away.

Nutrition Value:

- Calories: 252 Cal
- Fat: 18 g
- Carbs: 11 g
- Protein: 9 g
- Fiber: 5 g
- Net Carb: 6 g

Avocado Fries

Preparation time: 5 minutes
Cooking time: 5 minutes
Servings: 3

Ingredients:

- 3 medium avocados, peeled, pitted, sliced
- 1 1/2 cups almond meal
- 1/2 teaspoon salt
- 1/4 teaspoon cayenne pepper
- 1 1/2 cups avocado oil
- 1 egg

Method:

1. Take a shallow dish, add the almond meal and stir in salt and cayenne pepper until mixed.
2. Crack the egg in a bowl and then whisk until blended.
3. Coat a slice of avocado in egg, coat with almond meal mixture, and then fry in hot avocado oil in the skillet pan for 1 minute per side until golden brown.
4. When done, transfer fries to a plate lined with paper towels and then serve with mayonnaise.

Nutrition Value:

- Calories: 132 Cal
- Fat: 11.1 g
- Carbs: 6.6 g
- Protein: 4 g
- Fiber: 4 g
- Net Carb: 2.6 g

Zucchini Fries

Preparation time: 10 minutes
Cooking time: 10 minutes
Servings: 4

Ingredients:

- 2 medium zucchinis
- 1 cup almond flour
- 1/2 teaspoon garlic powder
- 1/2 teaspoon garlic salt
- 1/2 teaspoon paprika
- 1/2 teaspoon ground black pepper
- 1/2 cup grated parmesan cheese
- 1 tablespoon keto ranch dressing
- 1 egg

Method:

1. Switch on the oven, then set it to 400 degrees F and let it preheat.
2. Prepare the zucchini fries, and for this, cut zucchini into fries or wedges and then pat dry with paper towels.
3. Take a bowl, crack the egg in it and whisk until beaten.
4. Take a shallow dish, place almond flour in it, then add garlic powder, salt, paprika, and black pepper, cheese, and stir until mixed.
5. Dip a zucchini piece in the egg, then dredge with the almond meal mixture until coated, and arrange them on a baking sheet.
6. Spray oil over prepared zucchini fries and then bake them for 10 minutes until crispy and golden brown.
7. Serve fries with ranch dressing.

Nutrition Value:

- Calories: 121 Cal
- Fat: 9 g
- Carbs: 5 g
- Protein: 4.2 g
- Fiber: 3 g
- Net Carb: 2 g

Avocado and Egg Salad

Preparation time: 5 minutes
Cooking time: 0 minute
Servings: 6

Ingredients:

- 1/4 cup minced red onion
- 2 avocados, peeled, pitted, diced
- ½ teaspoon ground black pepper
- ½ teaspoon salt
- 2 teaspoons dill
- ½ of lemon, juiced
- 6 eggs, boiled

Method:

1. Dice the boiled eggs, place them in a bowl, then add avocado and stir well.
2. Add remaining ingredients, stir until combined, and then serve the salad straight away.

Nutrition Value:

- Calories: 160 Cal
- Fat: 12 g
- Carbs: 6 g
- Protein: 7 g
- Fiber: 3 g
- Net Carb: 3 g

Chapter 12: Desserts

Cookies

Preparation time: 15 minutes
Cooking time: 0 minute
Servings: 4

Ingredients:

- 1 cup shredded coconut, unsweetened
- 4 drops of stevia
- 2/3 cup peanut butter
- 2 tablespoons coconut butter

Method:

1. Take a heatproof bowl, add coconut butter in it, microwave for 30 seconds until it melts, and then stir peanut butter until combined.
2. Add coconut and stevia, stir until combined, and then spoon the mixture onto a sheet pan lined with parchment paper.
3. Spread the mixture evenly, freeze for 10 minutes, and then cut into eighteen cookies.
4. Serve straight away.

Nutrition Value:

- Calories: 80 Cal
- Fat: 8 g
- Carbs: 1 g
- Protein: 0 g
- Fiber: 0 g
- Net Carb: 1 g

Peanut Butter Mousse

Preparation time: 10 minutes
Cooking time: 0 minute
Servings: 4

Ingredients:

- ½ cup heavy whipping cream
- ½ teaspoon vanilla extract, unsweetened
- 1/4 cup peanut butter
- 1/4 cup Swerve Sweetener
- 4 ounces cream cheese, softened

Method:

1. Take a bowl, add whipping cream in it and beat until stiff peaks form, set aside until required.
2. Take another bowl, add peanut butter and cream cheese in it and beat until smooth.
3. Then beat in vanilla and sweetener until smooth and fold in whipped cream until combined.
4. Serve straight away.

Nutrition Value:

- Calories: 301 Cal
- Fat: 26.5 g
- Carbs: 5.6 g
- Protein: 6 g
- Fiber: 0.8 g
- Net Carb: 4.8 g

Chocolate Cake in a Mug

Preparation time: 5 minutes
Cooking time: 2 minutes
Servings: 1

Ingredients:

- 2 tablespoons almond flour
- 1/4 teaspoon vanilla extract, unsweetened
- 2 teaspoons coconut flour
- 1 1/2 tablespoons erythritol sweetener
- 1/2 teaspoon baking powder
- 2 tablespoons cocoa powder, unsweetened
- 2 tablespoons coconut butter, salted
- 1 egg

Method:

1. Take a heatproof bowl, add butter in it, and microwave for 25 seconds until butter melts.
2. Then stir in remaining ingredients, one at a time, and microwave for 1 minute or more until firm.
3. Top the cake with heavy cream and then serve straight away.

Nutrition Value:

- Calories: 405 Cal
- Fat: 37 g
- Carbs: 13 g
- Protein: 12.3 g
- Fiber: 7.2 g
- Net Carb: 5.8 g

Vanilla and Berry Mug Cake

Preparation time: 5 minutes
Cooking time: 2 minutes
Servings: 1

Ingredients:

- 2 tablespoons coconut flour
- 6 frozen raspberries
- 1/4 teaspoon baking powder
- 1 tablespoon erythritol sweetener
- 1 teaspoon vanilla extract, unsweetened
- 1 tablespoon coconut butter, melted
- 1 egg
- 2 tablespoons cream cheese

Method:

1. Take a heatproof bowl, add butter and cream cheese in it, and then microwave for 20 seconds.
2. Stir in flour, vanilla extract, baking powder, and sweetener until mixed and then whisk in the egg until combined.
3. Press berries into the batter and then microwave for 1 minute and 20 seconds until firm.
4. Serve straight away.

Nutrition Value:

- Calories: 342 Cal
- Fat: 27 g
- Carbs: 10 g
- Protein: 9 g
- Fiber: 5.5 g
- Net Carb: 4.5 g

Peanut Butter Mug Cake

Preparation time: 5 minutes
Cooking time: 1 minute
Servings: 1

Ingredients:

- 2 ½ tablespoons peanut butter
- 2 ½ teaspoon stevia, granulated
- 1 egg

Method:

1. Take a heatproof mix, add all the ingredients in it, and whisk until smooth and incorporated.
2. Microwave the cake batter for 1 minute at high heat setting until firm and then serve straight away.

Nutrition Value:

- Calories: 318 Cal
- Fat: 25 g
- Carbs: 9 g
- Protein: 15 g
- Fiber: 3 g
- Net Carb: 6 g

Raspberry Ice Cream

Preparation time: 5 minutes
Cooking time: 0 minute
Servings: 2

Ingredients:

- 1 cup frozen raspberry
- 1/8 teaspoon stevia powder
- ½ cup coconut cream

Method:

1. Place berries in a food processor, pulse for 1 minute until chopped, and then blend in sweetener and cream until smooth.
2. Serve straight away.

Nutrition Value:

- Calories: 242 Cal
- Fat: 22.4 g
- Carbs: 9.7 g
- Protein: 2.2 g
- Fiber: 4.3 g
- Net Carb: 5.4 g

Coconut Ice Cream

Preparation time: 4 hours and 10 minutes
Cooking time: 10 minutes
Servings: 4

Ingredients:

- 1/3 cup toasted shredded coconut, unsweetened
- 4 tablespoons powdered stevia
- 1 teaspoon vanilla extract, unsweetened
- 2 cups coconut cream
- 5 egg yolks
- 1 cup heavy cream

Method:

1. Take a heatproof bowl, place egg yolks in it and whisk until smooth.
2. Take a saucepan, add heavy cream and coconut cream, stir in sweetener and cook for 3 minutes or until bubbles start to appear around the edges.
3. Remove pan from heat, gradually whisk the egg yolks until incorporated, 1 tablespoon at a time, and then stir in vanilla until just mixed.
4. Return pan over medium-low heat, cook for 5 minutes until mixture reach to a custard consistency, then remove the pan from heat and let it cool completely.
5. Stir coconut in the ice cream mixture, then transfer the mixture in a large dish and freeze for 4 hours until frozen, stirring every hour.
6. Serve straight away.

Nutrition Value:

- Calories: 413 Cal
- Fat: 41 g
- Carbs: 6.5 g
- Protein: 5.5 g
- Fiber: 1 g
- Net Carb: 5.5 g

Strawberry Ice Cream

Preparation time: 5 hours and 10 minutes
Cooking time: 0 minute
Servings: 4

Ingredients:

- ¾ cup sliced strawberries, hulled
- 1/3 cup Swerve sweetener, granulated
- ½ teaspoon vanilla extract, unsweetened
- 2 cups heavy cream
- 2 tablespoons sour cream

Method:

1. Place all the ingredients in order into a food processor and pulse for 2 minutes until smooth.
2. Take an 8-inch loaf pan, pour the blended mixture in it, spread it evenly, and freeze for 3 to 5 hours until frozen, stirring every hour.
3. Serve straight away.

Nutrition Value:

- Calories: 296 Cal
- Fat: 29 g
- Carbs: 4 g
- Protein: 2 g
- Fiber: 1 g
- Net Carb: 3 g

Chocolate Ice Cream

Preparation time: 5 hours and 10 minutes
Cooking time: 10 minutes
Servings: 4

Ingredients:

- 1/4 cup cocoa powder, unsweetened
- 1 teaspoon xanthan gum
- 1/3 cup erythritol sweetener
- 1 cup heavy cream
- 1 teaspoon vanilla extract, unsweetened
- 1 cup almond milk, unsweetened
- 1 egg

Method:

1. Take a saucepan, add cocoa powder, then add remaining ingredients except for the vanilla and whisk well until smooth.
2. Heat the mixture over medium-low heat setting, bring it to a rolling boil, and continue cooking for 5 minutes to thicken the mixture so that it coats the back of a spoon.
3. Remove pan from heat, then whisk in vanilla, pour the mixture into a large container and then freeze for 3 to 5 hours until frozen, stirring every hour.
4. Serve straight away.

Nutrition Value:

- Calories: 247 Cal
- Fat: 24 g
- Carbs: 5 g
- Protein: 3 g
- Fiber: 2 g
- Net Carb: 3 g

Avocado Ice Cream

Preparation time: 5 hours and 10 minutes
Cooking time: 0 minute
Servings: 4

Ingredients:

- 2 small avocado, peeled, pitted, diced
- ¼ cup basil leaves
- ¼ cup of mint leaves
- ½ of lemon, juiced
- 2 tablespoons MCT oil
- 8.5 ounces of coconut milk, unsweetened

Method:

1. Place avocado slices in a food processor, pulse for 1 minute, then add remaining ingredients and pulse for 2 minutes until smooth.
2. Pour the mixture into a large container and then freeze for 3 to 5 hours until frozen, stirring every hour.
3. Serve straight away.

Nutrition Value:

- Calories: 226 Cal
- Fat: 23 g
- Carbs: 3 g
- Protein: 1.8 g
- Fiber: 1.7 g
- Net Carb: 1.3 g

Conclusion

The ketogenic diet is called a miracle diet because of its amazing benefits, easy to follow, and simple and budget-friendly cooking. But this brings another question – is keto diet for everyone? The ketogenic diet is a low carb diet with many health benefits, building muscles, reducing the chances of epilepsy, managing diabetes, and safeguarding from many chronic diseases. Above all, the keto diet has become famous for losing weight. But before trying out this diet, you must inquire about it with your doctor or nutritionist and see if it really suits you. With proper guidance and plan and foods, a keto diet will help you meet your health goals and will turn out most effective for your body than any other diet.

Lightning Source UK Ltd.
Milton Keynes UK
UKHW030942201020
371905UK00005B/369